THE TEACH YOURSELF BOOKS
EDITED BY LEONARD CUTTS

GEOLOGY

TEACH YOURSELF

GEOLOGY

By

A. RAISTRICK, M.Sc., Ph.D., M.I.Min.E.

Reader in Economic Geology, King's College.
University of Durham

THE ENGLISH UNIVERSITIES PRESS LTD
102 NEWGATE STREET
LONDON, E.C.I

First printed October 1943
This impression 1960

Printed in Great Britain for the English Universities Press, Limited,
by Richard Clay and Company, Ltd., Bungay, Suffolk

CONTENTS

LIST OF ILLUSTRATIONS

LIST OF ILLUSTRATIONS

CHAPTER I

INTRODUCTION

To call a person ' an old fossil ' conjures up a picture of a more or less inoffensive old man, a little musty, out of date in his thinking, and very unprogressive. It is a term of kindly tolerance mixed with pity and criticism. This picture would represent the attitude of many of the public to the science of geology, regarding it as a subject very remote from daily life, a suitable subject for the entertainment of absent-minded professors and rather old-fashioned members of the local Natural History Society. Geology is the antithesis of all this—it has a vital contribution that is being made daily to our everyday life and comfort in a thousand and one different contacts, no less real because they are not obvious. Many of our basic industries rely on the skill of the geologist to explore the crust of the earth and to find the raw materials they need; the civil engineer relies on the methods and technical knowledge of the geologist to advise on the safety of reservoir sites, the rocks likely to be met in tunnelling, the sources of pure underground water; in almost all sections of our trade and industries, as well as in the care of our public health, the science of geology plays a part. On its more theoretical side, geology links hands with many sciences—it unites with the mathematician to study and interpret earthquakes, and from them to deduce the structure of the earth's interior; with the chemist it makes a study of the composition of rocks and the varied products of volcanoes, and in mineralogy it shares the lore of crystal structures with the physicist. The biologist uses and interprets the fossil evidence of past forms of life that the geologist finds in the rocks of all past geological ages, and the story they reveal fills out the story of evolution, bridging many gaps that are left in the evidence derived only from living creatures.

With all these contacts, geology emphasises what all

branches of science teach: that they are indeed only different facets of a single body of knowledge, and the person who takes up geology as a study or a hobby will find much of interest and variety in these numerous extensions into the borderland of other subjects. The scope of geology is very wide, taking the whole world and its history for its sphere; it deals with the evolution of rocks and continents, as well as with the evolution of life; it deals also with time and with space. The conception of time that comes from the revealed story of millions of years during which processes have operated on the crust of the earth and during which evolution has proceeded by stages that are almost imperceptible according to our merely human measurement of time, gives a sense of stability and demands a controlled imagination that have very great cultural value. There is majesty and beauty in the procession of life as seen by the geologist, set against its background of a changing earth. To witness through the informed imagination the inception and growth of mountain ranges, to see them reduced to plains by the steady action of ordinary erosion, and to see the abundant evidence of a constantly moving life-stream, marked by the emergence of higher and higher forms, is to glimpse the tremendous power and certainty of evolution.

The importance of geology for the progress of the nation and its industries was recognised over a hundred years ago by the foundation of H.M. Geological Survey of Great Britain, a government department staffed by trained geologists who are charged with the task of investigating the geology of the country, preparing and publishing geological maps and memoirs to record it, and publishing special maps and memoirs on mineral resources, water supply, soils, and other matters of economic interest. Since the formation of the Survey in this country over one hundred and twenty other countries have formed Government geological surveys, mainly patterned upon our own, so that there is now no progressive country anywhere in the world without its official geological staff. The Geological Survey gives advice which for many decades has been the basis of all mining expansion in this country, and it is increasingly being called upon to help in matters of water supply, building materials, foundation sites, tunnelling, and so on. The staff of over forty geologists has been constantly used to supply basic information to committees considering many kinds of public work, and to examine and report upon mineral and other resources to take the place of those cut off by war, both during 1914–18 and at the present time. Advice was given on the water-power resources of Scotland, with notes on tunnel, canal, and dam sites; on the line of the mid-Scotland Canal scheme; on the proposed Severn and Mersey Tunnels, and on other large schemes that would take a chapter to enumerate. In some of the newer countries the Geological Survey is more directly linked with actual mineral prospecting than in this; in Russia the survey is called the Geological and Prospecting Service, and in the greater part of America the Surveys carry out a considerable amount of the actual exploration of new ground for mineral deposits, and even for location of actual mine sites and leases.

Geology as a science is primarily concerned with the history of the earth and the materials composing it, with the succession of events which has moulded the crust to its present state, and with the life that has lived upon that crust through past ages. The knowledge of the materials of the crust demands a special study of rocks, their properties and composition, and to this branch the special name **Petrology** has been applied. That part of the science which deals mainly with life-forms, now preserved as fossils, is called **Palæontology** (from the Greek words meaning ' ancient-life-knowledge '). **Applied geology** is the term used to cover the parts of geology that are particularly useful in mining, engineering, agriculture and other practical ways, and this has become sufficiently important in recent years to form a regular subject in itself, which is studied by most engineering and mining students during their University years. The old name **Stratigraphy** is applied to the study of strata—that is, to the rocks as they occur in the earth's crust in strata or layers, to their superposition and relation to one another, and to their history as shown by the contained fossils, their mineral composition, etc. Stratigraphy is actually the real summary of geology, the continuous story and history of the evolution of the solid earth and all that is upon and in it. The following diagram may be used to represent the relation of these differently named branches of the one subject.

PALÆONTOLOGY ——————— PETROLOGY
Study of fossils and their evolution. The environment in which they developed.   Chemical and mineral composition of rocks. Their mode of origin.

STRATIGRAPHY
Geological history of the earth.

PHYSICAL GEOLOGY
Processes which modify the crust of the earth. Weathering, mountains, earthquakes, volcanoes, etc.

APPLIED GEOLOGY
makes use of all in problems of industry and construction.

As the material used by geology is found everywhere in the crust of the earth, and the processes which have operated upon the crust to bring it to its present condition are known to have been the same in character from the earliest geological period as those which are now operating, it is obvious that much of the work of the geologist will consist of observation out of doors, or as we say ' in the field '. Geology is essentially an open-air subject, with indoor work in the study and laboratory based upon ' field-work '. There are thousands of good amateur outdoor geologists, many of whom have little acquaintance with the study and the laboratory, but there are very few ' armchair geologists ' who can work without a knowledge of the field-work.

Accepting the basic truth that the processes now at work on the crust of the earth are competent to explain all past changes, it follows that the geologist must give considerable attention to examining and understanding these processes. Every stream or river, lake or sea-shore offers to the careful observer instruction in some geological process or other, the effects of which process in past times may be recognised in the strata of a quarry or exposure of rocks and compared with the results of the process now operating. As his experience of present processes and their results grows, he will be able to reconstruct a true picture of some part of the past history of the rocks he observes. His knowledge of fossils will enable him to put an approximate date to the strata being examined in which the fossils occur, and a slight knowledge of minerals and petrology will often point to an economic value in rocks that otherwise seem to have little practical use. Over half a century ago a great geological teacher, Joseph Prestwich, summed up the matter thus: " The real classrooms of a geologist are to be found in quarries, pits, railway sections, cliffs, mountain passes, and ravines. To these the student must resort to obtain the mastery of the science which will enable him to interpret facts rightly and to draw conclusions justly. It is this direct study of nature, this exploration of ever new ground, this contact with scenery ever varied, this constant exercise of the powers of observation, with the seeing and handling of the forms of life long passed away, that give real geological knowledge and power. It is the acquisition of positive facts and the ever novel subjects of thought and reflection which the varied phenomena present, that constitute so great a charm and pleasure to those engrossed in special research, or to those merely in search of healthful change, new scenes and ideas, and recreation."

The field observations must be supported by adequate experience in the study, and if possible in the laboratory, and by the examination wherever possible of collections of rocks, fossils, and minerals in museums and private collections. The student must diligently collect and record his own material, however small and inadequate it may seem.   First-hand experience is the key to successful study as a geologist, and the trouble taken to secure and identify one's own specimens will impress their character on the mind in a way far more permanent and vivid than could be obtained by the same time spent in mere reading.

The Earth as a Planet.

As geology is concerned with earth-history, we must have some idea of the earth's origin and the earliest stages in its formation, but any detailed account of the earth as a planet belongs properly to the study of astronomy. We shall therefore take only the briefest outline of the stages in the birth of the earth, prior to the formation of a solid crust, from the story as revealed by recent astronomical and mathematical work, and consider it only so far as it throws light on the present condition of the earth's interior.

The earth is one of the planets revolving round the sun, and shares with all the other planets of the solar system in a common origin.   The material from which the planets are formed was torn from the parent material of the sun by a tidal disruption in the sun which occurred when another star approached and passed near to it; this happened at some very remote period.   The disruption produced a jet or filament of gaseous matter which was drawn out to a distance in space comparable with the orbit of the most distant planet.   From this jet the planets were formed by condensation of the gases around several nuclei, each nucleus becoming as it were the embryo of a different planet.   In the earliest stages of a condensing planet cloud the material would cool quickly, partly by the rapid radiation of its heat into space, and partly by the expansion of some of its gases.   The condensation resulted in a liquid core, and gradually, by continued cooling, the whole mass of each planet cloud became liquid.   Further loss of heat by radiation from the surface soon produced the first thin solid crust.   This first crust was a thin skin of crystalline igneous rock over the still-liquid interior, and this would act as a blanket, slowing down the radiation of heat. The heat from the interior now reached the surface only by conduction through the rock cover, and this was a considerably slower process than convection. After a very long time the next stage was accomplished, in which the interior of the earth solidified to approximately its present condition.

The physical properties of the interior of the earth can be investigated to some extent through the phenomena of earthquakes, the shock of which is transmitted through the substance of the earth's interior; the rate at which such shocks can travel through different depths of the earth is compared with their rate of travel through substances of differing density, rigidity, etc., in the laboratory, and, by analogy, some of the properties of the interior are deduced. A study of the magnetic behaviour of the earth and of variations in the earth's gravitational properties can also provide information. From many sources supplementary information is obtained, all of which can be integrated into a picture of the condition and composition of the earth's interior that fits in with the observed facts of geology at the surface and with our knowledge of such rocks and material as have from time to time been extruded at the surface from deep-seated sources.

The measurement of the density of rocks forming the crust of the earth shows that the continental areas are mainly composed of rocks and rock material with density ranging between 2·6 and 3. This crust of light material, if it could be spread in a uniform layer over the continents, would be only about half a mile thick ; in its thickest parts—that is, under the mountain ranges and high plateaus—this layer is probably not more than a few miles in thickness. Underlying this outermost crust of light rocks there is a zone of heavier crystalline rock with a density ranging from less than 3 to about 3·5, though the average is not much more than 3. There are several areas where these crystalline rocks, which mostly pre-date the sedimentary rocks, are exposed at the surface. These areas form the so-called Archæan shields—patches of very ancient rocks that have resisted most of the subsequent folding and alteration that have affected the newer strata; such shields form the greater part of the Canadian plains, the Baltic area, Central Africa, Western Australia, Peninsular India, North Eastern Asia, and Brazil. As the density of the earth taken as a whole is 5·5, the central 'core' must have a higher density, so that together with the much lighter crust they make this average figure. There is reason to believe that the density of the core is about 7 or 8. From several kinds of evidence it is now believed that below the heavy crystalline rocks that form the foundations of the continental areas there is a deep zone of mixed rock silicates and metals, mainly iron and magnesium, and occupying the centre, a core of nickel and iron.

Although these areas of ancient crystalline rocks are now reduced to approximate plains, or to areas of no very high relief, their structure shows them to be the worn-down remains of ancient mountain chains with some very complex structures. This suggests that they have experienced a very long and varied history before even the oldest of the sedimentary rocks with fossils were formed. The 'shield' areas may include fragments of the earliest solid crust that formed over the earth. As soon as such a crust formed and cooling had proceeded far enough for the condensation of water vapour from the atmosphere to take place in the form of rain, then erosion and weathering began. As the water gathered together in the irregularities of the crust to form lakes and seas, deposition of the material carried from the crust by moving water could take place. This initiated the 'cycle of deposition', and would be followed by all the other stages—uplift of deposits, renewed weathering and erosion, deposition of further material, formation of still newer deposits, and so on continuously. This succession of processes, once started, has gone on continuously at the surface and within the outer crust of the earth ever since. It can be represented in diagrammatic form as a 'cycle' or chain of events following one another in a definite order and being constantly repeated in the same order. Taking the earth as a whole, all stages of the cycle can be observed in operation at one part or another of the surface; weathering and erosion are at work on the continents, deposition is taking place in the seas, volcanic extrusion and igneous intrusion are at work in some of the mountainous areas, and metamorphism of materials is being accomplished in areas of subsidence.

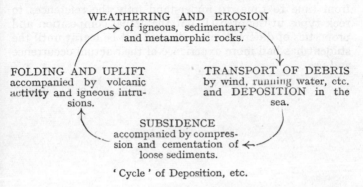

WEATHERING AND EROSION
of igneous, sedimentary and metamorphic rocks.

FOLDING AND UPLIFT accompanied by volcanic activity and igneous intrusions.

TRANSPORT OF DEBRIS by wind, running water, etc. and DEPOSITION in the sea.

SUBSIDENCE accompanied by compression and cementation of loose sediments.

' Cycle ' of Deposition, etc.

As the processes of weathering and erosion take place mainly on the exposed land surface of the earth, there is opportunity for the ordinary student to study them with less expense or special effort than would be needed to seek out and study examples of active volcanoes, or to investigate the floor of the ocean. The processes of weathering also are much more matters of everyday familiar things and therefore it will be easiest to start our systematic study of geology with these subjects and follow the ' cycle of deposition ' round through deposition and subsidence, treating next of volcanoes and the earthquakes which accompany mountain folding and uplift, and so completing the cycle in strict order. The second part of the book will deal with an outline of the geology of Britain, in which all these processes will find abundant exemplification. A later section will deal with the problems of geology applied to engineering and mining.

For all parts of the book some knowledge of geological terms and of the composition of the principal minerals making up the more important rock types will be necessary. It is probable that such description of minerals and terms will be needed frequently for reference, until they are learnt through frequency of use, and they are therefore placed in a separate chapter at the end of the book. The section on minerals and rocks will need to be read, and referred to from time to time, to understand fully the references to rock types in Chapter II, but the actual composition and properties of different minerals need not be learnt until the student has had more experience of their actual occurrence and use.

SECTION I. PHYSICAL GEOLOGY

CHAPTER II

Geological processes. Weathering: Water as weathering agent—chemical action; solvent action. Temperature—action of frost and heat. Wind—erosion by wind-blown sand. Loess formation. Erosion by running water. Erosion by ice.

WHENEVER rocks of any kind are elevated above the sea they are subjected to weathering, their components are broken down, and their bulk gradually disintegrated. The rock debris so formed is transported back to lower levels or to the sea by the action of gravity, the wind, and running water, and the process of re-deposition and formation of new strata goes on alongside the weathering and destruction of the old. We may break into this cycle at any point for the purpose of discussion, and so for convenience will start with the weathering of newly exposed rocks.

The principal weathering agents are the atmosphere, water and the sun's energy. These are overlapping in their effects, wind, rain and temperature changes accompanying one another, but their different methods of working are easily separable. Water from the oceans and lakes is raised into the atmosphere in the form of water vapour by the sun's energy. On condensation this water falls as rain or snow and accomplishes changes on the surface of the earth, partly by its solvent and chemical action and partly by its kinetic energy, which enables it to perform mechanical work. Rain-water in falling through the atmosphere takes into solution small quantities of atmospheric gases, the most important of which are oxygen and carbon dioxide. The oxygen in solution enables the water to act as an oxidising agent and the carbon dioxide forms with the water a weak acid, hydrocarbonic acid, which can act destructively on the rock-forming minerals and which can convert some rock components to carbonates. After a heavy discharge of lightning in a thunderstorm, traces of nitric and other acids are present in the air and small quantities are dissolved in the rain. Rain-water that has run over vegetation or over peaty ground also contains traces of organic acids, all of which hasten and strengthen its activity as a chemical reagent. If we consider the action of such acidulated water on exposed igneous rocks, we shall be able to trace the origin of much of the material of which the sedimentary rocks are made.*

The chief constituent minerals of igneous rocks (taking acid rocks with basic) are quartz, felspars, micas and the ferro-magnesian minerals. Of these the felspars, micas and ferro-magnesian minerals are easily attacked by the slightly acidulated rain-water, and from part of them sodium, potassium and calcium salts are formed, which are soluble in water. These soluble salts are washed out and carried away in streams and rivers to the sea and with other compounds present in small quantities, they make up the ' salt ' of sea-water. The part left behind is the completely insoluble silica (quartz) and silicates and oxides of aluminium and iron combined with water, which form the substances

QUARTZ—Silica, unchanged except for granulation, forming
    SAND (1)
FELSPARS—Potassium aluminium silicates,
    Sodium calcium aluminium silicates.

| Calcium taken out as carbonate— LIME (2) | Potash and Soda leached as soluble salts (3) | Aluminium hydrated silicates —CLAY (4) |

MICAS—Potassium aluminium silicate,
    Magnesium aluminium silicate.

| Magnesium carbonate (2) | Potash salts (3) | Aluminium silicates, etc. (4) |

FERRO-MAGNESIAN MINERALS—Iron magnesium calcium aluminium silicates.

| Iron hydrates and oxides (5) | Magnesium and calcium carbonates (2) | Aluminium hydrated silicates —CLAY (4) |

* See Chapter XVI for descriptions of minerals and rocks referred to in this section.

generally spoken of as clays. The principal changes can be shown in a simple tabular form, taking the rock-forming minerals in order and tracing the products derived from them by acid waters.

In the above scheme of chemical weathering there are five main groups of products, and these contribute as follows to the formation of new rocks.

(1) Sand. This is carried without chemical change to the sea, where it is deposited in river deltas, along the shore and in the shallow water. Eventually these sandy deposits become **sandstones**.

(2) The calcium and magnesium carbonates go to the sea in solution, and there certain plants and animals extract the lime (calcium carbonate) from the water and with it make their hard parts, shells or skeletons. The shells of most shell-fish, the skeletons of corals, sea-urchin shells and spines, and numberless minute animals called foraminifera all make use of the lime. These hard parts eventually fall to the sea floor and form a limy mud which is the parent material of **limestones**. The magnesium carbonate under certain conditions will combine with calcium carbonate to form the mineral ' dolomite ' (calcium magnesium carbonate), which is precipitated from solution in the form of a fine mud, and forms, on hardening, **magnesian limestone**.

(3) The soda and potash salts carried to the sea in solution are mostly changed to the chloride form by combination with chlorine, and when a portion of the sea becomes saturated with them—as for instance when an arm of the sea is cut off and dries up—they are deposited as **rock salt** (sodium chloride) and **potash** (potassium chloride). Such salt deposits usually contain other substances derived as these are from minerals present in the igneous rocks, but in smaller quantities than were those which we have discussed. These form rarer salts that sometimes occur with potash. Calcium will also form the sulphate of calcium, and this is deposited as the mineral **gypsum**.

(4) The aluminium remains partly as silicate and partly combined with oxygen and water to form the hydrate and oxide. The mixed aluminium silicate and hydrate is the basis of all **clay**. When very impure and mixed with rock

detritus of many kinds it will eventually form **shale**. Pure hydrated silicate of aluminium is often formed where granite rocks are weathering, and this is the mineral **kaolin or china clay**, used in the manufacture of porcelain.

The hydrated oxide of aluminium when fairly pure is called **bauxite**, and is the principal ore of aluminium, being smelted in an electric furnace for the production of the metal, and is also used in the preparation of many artificial abrasives.

(5) In tropical regions the chemical weathering and leaching of the soluble materials are hastened and carried to a greater extent. The product is then usually the material **laterite**, a reddish-brown clay, consisting of hydrated aluminium oxides mixed with oxides of iron and manganese. It is extensively formed from most igneous rocks, and in areas like the Deccan Plateau of India is an important ore of iron.

The first effect on rocks exposed to chemical weathering is to produce a thin outer skin of disintegrated and oxidised rock, usually coloured brown or red with the oxides or iron. If this is not washed off at once, it thickens from inside and eventually forms a thick crust. In selecting samples of rock in the field this must be remembered, and a hammer used to break into the ' fresh ' rock well below the weathered crust.

When structural work is built on an area of igneous rocks the chemical weathering may be a source of trouble or even of danger. Granites may be penetrated to a great depth by percolating waters which have produced residual clays adjacent to all the penetrating joints and cracks, and so the strength of the rock may be reduced almost to nothing. In Cornwall the kaolin from granite decomposition is occasionally found to extend as deep as 600 feet. In some reservoirs sited on an area of granite the extension in depth of the chemical weathering has necessitated unusually deep excavation at greatly increased cost to secure safe foundations and a water-tight trench for the dam.

The solvent action of water is seen at its maximum in areas of limestone rocks. When limestone is exposed at the surface in horizontal or gently inclined sheets, as in parts of the Pennines and Westmorland, and in County

Clare, Ireland, a peculiar topography is produced by the action of rain-water and streams. The surface of exposed limestone is fretted by the solvent action of the rain into a ' rippled ' texture, and deep ' run-off ' channels are formed along the sloping slabs. These channels often run together just as do small streams, and so concentrate the water on one spot. As soon as the run-off meets a joint (within a few feet at most) it finds a way down the joint, quickly dissolving the sides and producing an open crack that may be many feet deep. As all the joints are thus opened a pavement is produced with isolated blocks of limestone in a rectangular maze of open joints at intervals of about a yard apart. All soil is sooner or later carried down the opened joints, and a bare rocky area of exposed limestone left behind. Where much water is concentrated at one spot a ' pot-hole ' will be produced—a larger and deeper shaft down which the water falls to great depths. From pot-holes the drainage escapes by channels along bedding planes, dropping to lower levels by further under-ground pot-holes or caves, and eventually reaching a level of permanent saturation, or an impervious floor. From this level in a district with deep valleys the water may escape through powerful springs, or even emerge from a limestone cave as a river. As the limestone joints are widened and more water goes underground, former surface streams become dried up and their valleys are left streamless. Any limestone plateau is thus characterised by ' clints and grikes ' (the blocks and enlarged joints), by pot-holes, underground water-courses and by dry valleys.

The water that goes underground in a limestone area is heavily charged with calcite in solution and may, in a free space such as a cave, deposit some of that calcite as it evaporates. In a cave the re-deposited calcite forms tapering cylindrical masses of crystalline calcite, those hanging from the roof called ' stalactites ', those standing up from the floor, ' stalagmites '. Much of the calcite is re-deposited in shapeless masses, and at springs is formed round mosses and vegetation. This gives a spongy mass as the plant-stuff decays ; such spongy calcite is called **tufa.**

On sandstones and other granular rocks, water often hastens their disintegration by dissolving away the cementing material between the grains of quartz. The loosened skin of grains is washed away and a fresh lot of cement exposed to the rain. This action is most effective when the cement is either calcite or carbonate of iron, two of the commonest soluble cements.

The mechanical effect of falling rain-water is best seen on exposures of a clay containing boulders of rock, such as a glacial boulder-clay. The impact of the rain is sufficient to wash away slight amounts of the softened clay and any sandy patches, but has no visible effect on the pebbles and boulders. In time boulders are almost isolated, the clay around them being washed away, but that underneath them being protected as by an umbrella, so that they are left perched on a pedestal. This action continues, the pedestal growing more slender until the boulder topples over and exposes the patch of clay to fresh weathering. On a small scale this action can be seen in most clay banks that are exposed to direct rainfall. The impact and washing of the rain are an important factor in the breaking down of soil freshly exposed by ploughing.

Temperature Changes.

Changes of temperature achieve the breakdown of rock material in two main ways: (a) directly and (b) through the intermediary of water. In the direct action, particularly in areas where there is a great difference between day and night temperatures, the rocks exposed to direct sunlight during the day are warmed and the heat penetrates inward for some depth. As the minerals composing the rock have different coefficients of expansion—that is, they expand by different amounts for the same rise of temperature—the heating sets up great strains and stresses between the different crystals. With the cooling contraction takes place and this action repeated day after day will soon reduce the crust of the rock to a granular state. In parts of Africa the range of temperature between day and night may be over 100° F. Livingstone in his *Journal* of travels in the

Zambesi area records that rock surfaces were occasionally heated up to 137° F. at noon, and then cooled so rapidly at night that sharp angular fragments, from a few ounces to over 100 lb. in weight, were split off. As the action is strongest on exposed corners and edges, a rock exposed to high temperature variation soon becomes rounded, and further disintegration proceeds by the breaking loose of successive skins, like the skins of an onion being peeled. This ' peeling ' is called **exfoliation**.

In all areas subjected to frost, water is a powerful agent of destruction of rocks. Joints which are either fine capillary cracks, or larger joints partly filled with earth or detritus, hold water after rain. When this freezes it expands by one-ninth of its volume, with almost irresistible force. This expansion forces the joints wider open, making room for a larger quantity of water, so that on the repetition of freezing a still greater force operates. This effect is soon cumulative to the stage of splitting and detaching large masses from a cliff-face or from an exposed outcrop. It proceeds on all scales, and is responsible for much of the reduction of fallen rock material. On the smallest scale it is a valuable asset to the farmer and gardener, reducing their turned-up soil to a fine state of tilth.

Wind Erosion.

The wind in itself has little effect on exposed rock, but as an agent picking up and carrying fine sand and rock particles it becomes powerful to erode even the hardest rocks. A strong wind will pick up quite large particles of sand and carry them some distance along a curved path before they fall to the ground. These grains, usually of quartz, are hurled against any obstacle in the line of the wind, and act as a powerful ' sand-blast '. The largest particles are carried near the ground level, and even gentle winds can trundle small particles along near the ground, so that an upstanding rock shows excessive wind erosion at its base, and may be considerably undercut. Softer layers in the rock are etched out much deeper than hard layers and fantastic shapes may result. The impact of sand on the rock breaks off very minute angular fragments of rock minerals, and this fine dust is carried away by the wind to quieter areas and there deposited. This wind-blown dust may be deposited to great thicknesses in areas where there are constant winds for a great part of the year. Bordering the desert areas of Asia there are, particularly in north and west China, enormous areas of such dust, accumulated to a depth of more than 1000 feet. As it is deposited grasses and other tall vegetation are smothered, but struggle through the accumulating dust, forming an appreciable vertical ' bind '. As the dust—or, to give it its geological name, loess—consists of fresh mineral particles, and is very porous, it is immediately subject to chemical weathering by such rain as falls. The carbonates, particularly lime, which are thus formed run down the decayed stems of grasses and line them with re-deposited calcite. This strengthens the loess and gives it a characteristic vertical jointing. In areas where it is thick the loess is strong enough to be cut into cave dwellings. The rivers run through loess cut valleys that are marked by high vertical sides, the dominant breakage of the loess being everywhere vertical.

In sandy desert areas the wind is active in forming sand-dunes, asymmetric piles of sand which are constantly shifting. In the movement the wind rolls grains of sand up the windward side and tips them over the crest to roll down the leeward slope of the dune. In this process the grains are rubbed and knocked together, and fine detritus is produced that goes to form loess. The wind-blown sand grains acquire a very fine polished surface and a spherical shape that is produced in no other way. A pinch of desert sand seen even through a low-power hand lens has this rounded and polished character, so that it is called ' millet-seed ' sand. In several ancient sandstones, such as the New Red Sandstone of Permian and Triassic age, this character is seen on the constituent grains, and along with other evidence is proof that these ancient rocks accumulated under desert conditions.

Erosion by Running Water.

This is probably the most widespread and powerful agent of erosion at present at work on the earth's surface. Wherever rain falls and the water runs to the sea or to lakes in streams, erosion is going on rapidly. The action of the water depends on several factors. The impact and kinetic energy of moving water exert great pressure on any obstacles in its way, and are powerful to move rocks and rock fragments in its path. Like the wind, when flowing rapidly it has power to pick up and carry for short distances small fragments of material and thus exerts a tearing action at the bed over which it is running. Armed with lifted and moved rock fragments, it becomes a powerful cutting agent, battering pebbles and sand-grains against banks and rocks, grinding the moving fragments against one another and reducing both large and small to smaller sizes. The action of the water is assisted by its power to remove and transport the debris produced, so exposing fresh surfaces for erosion. The transporting power of a running stream depends on two principal factors: (a) the volume and velocity of the stream, and (b) the specific gravity, shape and size of the fragments handled. It is generally accepted (after the work of Hopkins and Stevenson) that the transporting power of a stream increases as the sixth power of its velocity—i.e., if the velocity of a stream is doubled, the transporting power increases by two to the sixth, which is sixty-four times. This enables much larger material to be moved. At a velocity of approximately $1\frac{1}{3}$ miles per hour, a stream will roll along rounded gravel up to 1 inch diameter; at about 2 miles per hour angular stones the size of an egg will be moved along, and at the velocities of a great flood, boulders many feet in size may be moved. As the average rock material has a specific gravity about 2·65, in the water it has considerable buoyancy, and a rock loses from a half to a third of its weight in air when entirely submerged. This enables very large masses of rock to be moved, which, even if moving with low velocity, acquire enormous kinetic energy and become powerful tools for breaking down other obstructions and for grinding other rocks.

By the grinding and cutting of the transported debris, the banks and floor of a river channel are constantly cut and polished, all roughnesses being smoothed off. Where a rock floor is exposed, and there is an irregularity in which a boulder can lodge in all but flood states of the stream, ' pot-holes ' are likely to form. These are circular-sectioned holes drilled in the rock floor by the rotation and rocking of the large boulder, armed with the sand and rock fragments that lodge beneath it; at many states of the stream there will be enough rush of water to rock and roll the larger stones, even if they cannot be carried away.

Smaller stones are carried round by every eddy current, and grind and scour the stream-bed into innumerable pot-holes, large and small. In time the pot-holes approach one another as they increase in size and the partition between them breaks away, leaving a narrow rock gorge with sides cut in finely polished concave sweeps. The cusps between these are attacked, and in time a rock gorge is produced through which the stream rushes with great velocity and cutting power. As the downward-cutting power of the stream is related to its ' grade ', it is constantly reduced as the stream-bed gets lower and slower. As this takes place, some of the energy is directed laterally to the banks, and the original narrow gorge is widened out by erosion of the banks and by removal of harder obstacles. If we take a view of the whole length of a river course, we can separate it into at least three main portions. In the high country, hills or mountains, the stream is small in volume but swift running, supplied with ample amounts of coarse rock material from the weathering of steep hill-slopes and exposed rock outcrops; this part is characterised by deep channels and rock gorges, pot-holes and waterfalls. The irregularities of the stream-bed are at a maximum, and the valley is narrow and rugged. Such a stream would be called ' juvenile ' or ' immature '. As the stream leaves the higher hills, the valley widens, the stream is increased in volume by increased gathering ground for run-off water and the conjunction of tributaries, and the rougher features disappear. Waterfalls are usually low and broad, gorges are absent and the current is slower. The greater part of all the work of the stream in this portion is expended in transporting fine material held in suspension in the water, and in cutting at the banks of the river. This is the 'mature' part of the river valley. Finally, as sea-level is approached, the river becomes larger and more sluggish, the valley bottom is filled with flood-plains of wide extent, and all gorges, waterfalls and other irregularities of the bed have disappeared. This is the 'flood-plain' of the river.

The sides of a river valley are exposed to the weathering by rain and frost and wind, and broken-off rock materials form 'screes'—heaps of small rock fragments with very little soil, which move down the hillside under the pull of gravity, finding their way down to the stream side. The stream cuts into the toe of the scree and removes material as quickly as it accumulates. This scree-stuff is abraded and used by the stream in its cutting of bed and banks, so that stream erosion and weathering together are constantly cutting at the valley sides and widening it. In floods great quantities of scree material that may tend to choke the stream-floor are removed, and the stream is given a fresh start. In the juvenile portion of the valley irregularities in the bed are at a maximum. In an area of differing strata there will be some stratum harder than its immediate neighbours, and erosion of this will be slower than of the rest. In time it will stick out above the rest in the stream course and pond up the water behind it, reducing its velocity. As the stream cutting is thus reduced above the obstruction, it is at the same time increased below as the water falls over the barrier—its energy of fall cutting the softer rock underneath into a deep hollow. In this way a waterfall is produced, and erosion is concentrated at the lip and in the pool below the fall. The softer rocks below are rapidly cut back by the impact of the water and by the enhanced erosion, helped by constant soaking with spray and the churning of gravel and boulders in the pool below. This action undercuts the lip of the fall, and from time to time pieces are broken off and the position of the lip is moved a little upstream. This action is more rapid than the weathering of the valley side, so that a gorge is produced, with the waterfall at its head, and this will continue until the lip of obstruction is carried back as far as the normal curve of the stream course. At that time cutting will again reassert itself on the valley sides, the gorge will be opened out and a normal valley produced. We can best picture a stream in its juvenile portion as having a limited amount of energy which it always directs towards the most prominent points. As these are removed one by one, its action becomes more widespread, the final objective being a smooth, uniformly curved valley, both lengthwise and sideways.

In the maturer part of the valley the stream is still constantly handling and shifting material, but here its progress is more like that of the crab—there is considerable sideways action in it. Any slight irregularity in slope or texture will cause the stream to deflect from a perfectly straight-line course and make a bend. In passing round the bend the current is deflected from the convex bank and strikes into the concave bank, to be again deflected towards its original course. This concentrates the attack of the current on the concave bank, undercutting it, picking up and carrying away material and thus emphasising the bend. On the convex bank gravel and other material drop in the quiet water and a gravel spit is soon built up (Fig. 1). In effect the river is constantly making its course more sinuous and building up loops sideways. These also move downstream, as there is greater pressure and cutting on the downstream part of the bend, and the bottom of the loops will sag and move downstream. In time the loops become very complete, with only a narrow neck at one end, which sooner or later, in time of flood, breaks through, cutting off the loop and straightening the course of the stream. These great loops are called ' meanders ', and when cut off will produce an ' ox-bow '. In the making and moving of meanders the gravel is ground and abraded and great quantities of smaller material produced, which is carried away by the stream. As the stream enters the plains nearly at sea level, this finer material is deposited as the current slows and forms ' alluvium ' or river ' silt '. At times of flood sand and coarser silt are carried right to the sea, and at all times quantities of the finer silt are transported, and finally dropped in the quiet waters of the sea where the river current dies out.

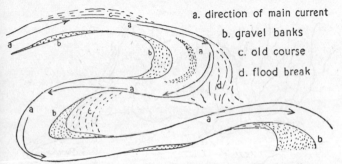

a. direction of main current

b. gravel banks

c. old course

d. flood break

FIG. 1.—River Meanders in Wharfe near Kettlewell.

Where a whole system of small streams originate on a sloping countryside, there will be great competition between them, and what is called ' river-capture ' may take place. If one stream has an initial advantage in its cutting—either greater supplies of water, or softer strata in which to cut its valley—it will soon cut to a lower level than an adjacent stream. On the flanks of the ridge between two streams the tributaries flowing to the one that has cut deeper will have a greater fall, a greater velocity and an increased cutting power, and will therefore cut at the bed and sides of the valley with greater effect. As the valley-head is cut back by erosion, it will soon intersect the upper part of the ridge common to both, and cut into the upper parts of the tributary of the slower stream. In time it may cut so far as to intersect the main adjacent stream, and then divert the upper waters of that stream through its new-cut gap into its own drainage. This is called ' river-capture ', and the effect is cumulative, as the volume and cutting power of the capturing stream are increased and the captured stream loses some of its supplies and is weakened in proportion. This process is very widespread, and is responsible for the complex pattern of most of the river drainage in Britain. One practical effect of such capture may be that the capturing river brings into its own valley far more water than the valley could normally accommodate,

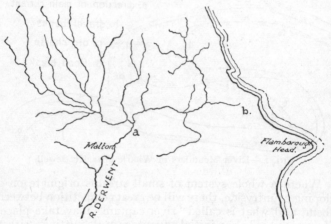

FIG. 2.—River Capture.

Capture of the drainage of the North Yorkshire Moors, by the river Derwent at (a), old exits of rivers to the sea stopped at (b) by glacial deposits.

and flooding may become a serious problem in its lower reaches. Both streams will be misfits, one too large and the other too small for its valley (Fig. 2).

It is by continued and repeated captures that a mature river system is built up, and the extent of these completed ' captures ' is some measure of the age of a river system. In England such a system as that draining to the sea by the Humber is an old and complex group with a long history of river-captures behind it. The Ouse–Humber rivers have added to themselves at various times all the rivers of the eastern slopes of the Pennines from the Swale to the Trent, and also the Derwent in East Yorkshire and its tributaries from the North Yorkshire Moors.

In the lower and middle courses of a river valley the alluvium and gravels of the flood-plain are often arranged in ' terraces ' lying at slightly different levels along the valley sides. This is evidence of the intermittent lowering of the base level to which the river is cutting down its bed— either the sea level has been lowered, or the land has risen. A flood-plain is formed when a river has cut down very nearly to its base level (sea level) and when its sideways meanders are at a maximum. If at this stage the sea level is lowered, the river is given renewed cutting power— ' rejuvenation '—and will again attack the valley floor, cutting a new valley through the alluvial plain. When this is repeated before the river has had time to remove all the old gravels, portions of the flood-plain will be left in the concave sides of the valley, having a level surface at the old flood-plain level. Each rejuvenation will be marked by sets of terrace fragments; these are ' river terraces ', and in most British river valleys four or five, or even more, river-terrace levels will be found.

Erosion by Ice.

In many mountainous parts of the world, as well as in the Arctic and Antarctic areas, the higher ground is covered by snow, which is spoken of as permanent snowfield, and as lying ' above the snow-line '. The area above the snow-line is simply that part of the earth's surface where temperatures are such that all precipitation is in the form of snow, and where the melting and ' run-off ' of snow in summer are entirely balanced by the snowfall, so that the ground is permanently covered to great depth with snow and ice. The snow added each year must find an escape from the area, or the accumulation would reach fantastic and impossible amounts. The escape is mainly effected in three ways: there is a certain amount of ' dry ' evaporation of the surface of the snow, under the influence of dry winds; a part of the snow falls down the steeper slopes under

B—GEOL.

the pull of gravity, forming avalanches; the greatest part of the 'run-off', however, is in the form of ice moving under gravity. These ice-streams or 'glaciers' owe their formation to the curious physical properties of snow and ice. When snow accumulates to great depth, the pressure due to its weight quickly transforms the basal layers of snow to a form of ice. Snow is crystallised (frozen) water, and consists of extremely complex feathery crystals, belonging to the hexagonal system. Under pressure the delicate crystals are broken, and produce a felted mass of ice spicules. Under increased weight or pressure the freezing point of water is lowered a few degrees, and at the points of contact of the ice spicules melting takes place, the melt-water moving into spaces between the spicules, where it immediately re-freezes. As this is continued indefinitely, the mass gradually assumes the form of a solid, nearly homogeneous (equal structure) mass of ice. Under the pull of gravity this ice will 'flow' partly by sliding over the floor on which it rests, partly by melting and re-freezing between individual crystals. The glacier ice has thus a certain amount of fluidity, and a glacier in many respects acts exactly like a river, when due allowance is made for the greater viscosity and brittleness of its material.

In recent geological ages glaciers and ice-sheets extended over the greater part of North-west Europe and Northern America, as well as over some other parts of the world now free of ice. The erosion caused by that period of glaciation is therefore prominent in most of the scenery of this part of the world, and can be studied to perfection in most parts of Britain north of the Thames.

The ice-stream carries out its erosion, as does a river, partly by 'plucking' at its floor and valley sides, and partly by the grinding and abrading of the material it picks up. Ice has the power to freeze on to irregularities of rock, and so, as gravity exerts its pull, there is a strong disruptive force, which can tear off large as well as small rock fragments. Near the glacier the disruptive action of freezing water is intensified by the difference between night and day temperatures, and the rock debris broken off any exposure of rock falls down the valley sides on to the glacier. When ice is moving, the centre of the stream flows with greater velocity than the sides and bottom; and as ice is brittle, cracks and fissures are produced by the strain of the different movement. These cracks go to great depth in the ice, and are called ' crevasses '. Rock debris falling on to the glacier is carried along on the surface, strung out in long gravel ridges called ' moraines ', but some of the material falls into the crevasses, and, as they open and close, is broken and abraded to smaller grains, some of it finding its way right through the ice to the ' sole ' of the glacier. Here it is frozen into the sole and acts like the teeth of a file, to grind away at the rocks over which the ice passes. Where any glacier has passed, all rocky promi- nences in its bed are rounded and polished by this grinding into a characteristic shape—the upstream side is in a perfect streamlined curved surface, the downstream side is plucked and torn into an irregular butt-end. Such a rounded rock is called a ' roche moutonnée ', from its like- ness to a sheep when seen in the distance on the mountain slopes. The Lake District is full of magnificent examples of such polished rocks of all sizes, from the smallest up to whole mountain summits which have been smoothed and shaped. All the rocks that ice has travelled over are deeply scratched and scored by the stones frozen into the ice and may be very deeply grooved in some cases. Such scratches and groovings are called ' striations ', and their general direction can be used as evidence of the direction of movement of the ice. The grinding action of the rock- loaded ice is not confined to the valley floor, but is exerted against every sinuosity of the valley side, so that projecting angles are ground off and irregularities smoothed down. A valley that has been occupied by a glacier is thus detected by the deepening of its floor in smooth curves and the truncation and polishing of spurs that extend into it. After continued glaciation a valley receives a cross-section that resembles a capital U, in contrast to a river valley, which is more like a V in section. Such a glaciated valley is referred to as a U-valley.

As a glacier descends from above the snow-line it reaches warmer levels, and melting at the front takes place as well as increased melting at the base of the ice. Under the glacier there are streams of melt water, confined in narrow passages under the ice, where their erosive power, armed with the finer debris penetrating the crevasses, is very great. In the bottom of a U-valley it is therefore to be expected that deeper gorges, pot-holes and other features of intensive water erosion will be found. The glacier ends at a level where the annual melting of the ice just balances the annual supply moving forward down the glacier. If the annual melting increases, then the front edge or 'snout' of the glacier will gradually be found higher up the valley each year—the glacier will be said to be retreating; if the melting is less than the supply, then each year it will extend a little lower, and will be said to be advancing. As a glacier retreats, the morainic material carried on its surface is dumped over the snout and left as large gravel mounds across the valley, through which the melt-water stream cuts a way. Such moraines cross many of the valleys of this country, and the period since the Ice Age has not been long enough for all of them to be removed by river erosion. It is good practice to explore a hilly or mountainous district, recording U-valleys, striated rocks, roches moutonnées, moraines, etc., and from them to reconstruct a picture of the glaciation. Any part of Wales, the Pennines, the Lake District or Scotland will supply abundant material.

CHAPTER III

Marine Erosion.

THE greater part of all the erosive action of the sea is confined to the narrow strip of coastline extending from a little below low water to a short distance and height above high-water mark. Although coastal erosion is going on along most of the coasts of the world, and is often very intense, the area of its operation is very small when compared to the total area of the earth's crust exposed to the other forms of erosion already discussed.

The prime source of the erosive power of the ocean is the energy of the tidal movements, derived from the gravitational pull of the moon on the earth. The tides produced occur twice in each twenty-four hours, and go on ceaselessly throughout geological periods, and therefore in the aggregate are a very powerful agent in accomplishing geological changes. The range of the tides varies considerably in different areas and conditions, the lowest range being found in some of the enclosed seas, such as the Mediterranean, where it varies between 4 and 10 inches at its lowest, up to 5 to 6 feet in the bay of Gibraltar. In the case of coastlines exposed to the full tidal current and with enclosed bays or estuaries, the tides may reach as much as 60 or 70 feet rise and fall. The tidal current passes very swiftly across open ocean, and when it enters a rapidly narrowing coastal inlet the water is crowded together into a smaller area, and consequently piles up to greater height and increases its velocity. The drag of friction on the floor and sides of the channel will cause the oscillations of the water particles to pile up into waves, and these may rush up an inlet with great speed and a high crest. The so-called ' bore ' of the Severn estuary is caused in this way. The tidal current entering the estuary is rapidly constricted and a large wave is built up, with a crest 8 or 9 feet high, which rushes up the river with increasing velocity until it is finally overcome by the friction and resistance of the river channel. The tides at Chepstow thus amount to a maximum rise of 50 feet. Against a shelving shoreline the friction of the floor again piles up the tidal current into waves which acquire both great height and velocity. A point is soon reached where the wave becomes top heavy, the base being slowed down by the frictional drag, and then the wave 'breaks', overturning and falling on to the shore. As the wave often contains many tons of water and waves are continuously breaking and dashing against a coast, there is in effect a bombardment which in total reaches even in one day, an almost astronomical figure when measured in weight of water falling. The energy of the breaking waves is dissipated in shifting the beach material about, in erosion and transport of material.

The erosion of a shoreline can be studied under four main processes, for the purpose of clarity:

(a) The energy of the breaking waves and tidal currents has an actual tearing power on the coast material comparable to the plucking of a river or glacier;

(b) water is forced under great pressure into cracks and joints of rocks forming the coast, and exerts a disruptive pressure, tearing rocks apart along any lines of weakness;

(c) in many cases a wave breaking against a shoreline traps large quantities of air under its falling crest, and this is compressed under the weight of the wave, and, rushing into cracks, exerts a pressure in the same way as the water does, but has power to penetrate much deeper into the rocks;

(d) waves can pick up and move loose detritus, rock fragments and sand and gravel, abrading them together and breaking them down, and also hurling them against the shore and effecting direct erosion and abrasion. The hardest cliffs are soon cut and abraded in this fashion.

These processes can best be explained by the use of actual measured and recorded examples.

(a) The weight of falling waves has been measured on many occasions, as it is an important consideration in the design of harbour and other coastal structures that have to resist it. Stevenson found that a wave of ground swell 20 feet high falls with a pressure of approximately 1 ton per square foot. The force of breakers on the Atlantic and North Sea shores has been measured at 611 lb. per square foot in summer and 2086 lb. per square foot in winter. The maximum pressure recorded was at Dunbar, where 3½ tons per square foot was measured, and at several other places 3 tons was recorded. It is clear that a pressure of this order against the side of a pier or harbour work that is directly opposed to the run of the tide may mount up to very large figures. The power of this falling water to pick up and move material is illustrated by the following examples. In measurements at a harbour site, with a maximum wave of 6 feet high, rip-rap (that is stone ballast) from 40 to 200 lb. weight of individual blocks was picked up and moved from all the ground between 2 feet and 10 feet above mean water level. Breakers moved slabs of concrete of 350 lb. weight at 7 feet above mean water, and a block of concrete 10 ft. × 6 ft. × 2½ ft. (21,000 lb. wt.) was lifted 3 inches and wedged fast in a new position. On several sea fronts large blocks of stone or concrete of 1 or 2 tons weight have been moved several yards out of position. The height to which storm-waves may exert pressure when breaking is surprisingly exemplified at Unst, the northernmost point of the Shetland Islands. There in a great storm walls were overthrown and a door torn open at a height of 196 feet above sea level. At Bound Skerry, Shetland, blocks weighing from 6 to 13½ tons were torn out of the original bed at heights up to 70 feet above high-water level. On any cliff-face where the rock is well jointed frost action will soon loosen a block, and storms may quickly shift it further, once loosened. In this way a well-jointed cliff of rock is quickly disintegrated.

(b) The rush of water under the pressure of a breaking

wave will penetrate joints in the rocks, will enter caves and fissures, and move jointed blocks from their bed. This is probably one of the main contributory actions in the movement of large blocks already described under (a). It must be remembered that when the rock is completely covered by water the effect of buoyancy in reducing the weight to be moved must be taken into account. If all the fissures surrounding a rock mass can be penetrated and filled by water, then the effect of the hydraulic pressure added to the buoyancy allows other erosive action to have more effect.

(c) The waves running up a beach will be seen to have a crest curving over towards the land, and at the point of breaking this curve is actually a considerable over-hang. If a wave is so related to a cliff face or the shore that it falls before it breaks into spray, it will trap a considerable volume of air beneath it, and compress it by its falling weight. The air may blow the wave to spray, hurling up jets of water high in the air—these are the high seas so eagerly watched at seaside resorts. The compressed air may, on the other hand, be driven into the cracks and crannies of the rocks, and will have the same effect towards disrupting them as the water forced in. In time the combined effect of water and air will enlarge a joint, and sand and rock fragments hurled about by the tides will abrade until such a joint cave may penetrate for a long distance into the cliff. In time a hole may be broken through at the far end, to the surface, and then a ' blower ' is formed. Water rushing into the cave is forced through the inner hole, and spouts into the air in a great plume. This is an early stage in the opening up of a deep inlet, which in time becomes a narrow, gorge-like rift in the cliffs, from which the sea is able to make lateral attack on the sides. Holes drilled in this way along two sets of joints sometimes produce a natural arch, which in turn may collapse, leaving a free-standing pillar or ' stack ' of rock standing out from the general line of cliff. All these forms are stages in the penetration and disrupting of a line of cliffs by marine action, and none of them has any permanence.

(d) Waves and currents along shore toss up large quantities of rock debris, sand and gravel, and by their impact on the cliff foot hasten the erosion in a zone extending for a few feet above high-water mark. By this intensified local action a cliff face is undercut, and as the undercutting reaches back to a main joint, there will be a large-scale collapse of cliff material. This for a time shrouds the cliff foot and takes much of the energy of the waves in its further abrasion and reduction of size. As the material is reduced and removed, direct attack on the cliff is renewed and the cycle of events is constantly repeated. If the rocks of the cliff are disposed with horizontal bedding and the joints vertical, the erosion can be regarded as proceeding at an average rate. If the dip or slope of the rocks is towards the land, then there will be a condition of maximum stability, and erosion will be slow. When the dip is towards the sea, erosion proceeds with maximum speed, as gravity will assist the movement of rock-masses down the dip slope and the joints and bedding planes in the rock will be constantly lubricated with water forced along them. In such conditions large slips of cliff material are inevitable, and wastage proceeds at a great rate (Fig. 3).

The material picked up on the beach by an incoming wave is carried some way up the beach, then, as the wave runs back, sand and pebbles are carried down the beach again by the scour of the water. In this way beach material is in constant motion. In times of excessive storm beach material is flung far up a shelving shore and may be piled in a mound at a height considerably above ordinary tides. Such a mound may remain for years, between storms, and is spoken of as a storm beach. This constant movement of beach material produces a rough grading in size, the larger material at the head of the beach, grading to finer gravel, and then to sands towards the low water. The finer rock-flour and mud are carried right away to sea as quickly as they are produced, so that where erosion is active the beach materials are kept clean and constantly re-exposed to abrasion.

The removal of a strip of land from around the coast by

erosion has naturally attracted attention from many practical points of view, and frequent attempts have been made both to measure the actual loss by erosion and to arrest its progress. The erosion of a coastline is naturally related to the nature and texture of the rocks composing it, to the structure of the coast, and to the onset of tides and currents. Where a coast consists of cliffs of uniform hard rocks in a stable structure, the rate of erosion is

FIG. 3.—Coast Erosion in Magnesian Limestone, Co. Durham.

slow. In the report to a committee investigating this problem in 1888, it is said that the cliffs of Magnesian Limestone between the mouths of the Tyne and Wear, in Durham, were being worn away at a rate of about 1 inch in fifty years. There is evidence that that rate has been exceeded recently, possibly by reason of the extensive coast and pier works near the Tyne having altered the tidal and coastal currents. The erosion on this coast is most evident in the detached 'stacks', which within living memory have been considerably reduced in area. Where the structure of a coast is very varied, with alternations of hard and soft rocks and varied dips, the coast is worn into a most irregular pattern. The erosion proceeds rapidly on the softer and more unstable rocks and eats out deep inlets along them, leaving the harder ones projecting as headlands or skerries. Erosion proceeds most rapidly where the coastline is formed of clays or of partially consolidated, or even unconsolidated rock. In such cases the erosion proceeds with great regularity and the coastline retreats uniformly inland.

Examples of the latter case are numerous along the east coast of England and in parts of the Lancashire coastline, all of them areas where the land is composed either mainly of boulder clay and gravels from the Ice Age, or of the later unconsolidated deposits of Tertiary times, such as the beds on the East Anglian coast. There are abundant measured examples in such areas, of which only a few need be given here. South of the mouth of the Thames, on the coast between Sheerness and Ramsgate, between the years 1872 and 1896 the sea encroached at Herne Bay a distance of 1300 feet—that is, a removal of the coast at a rate of over 50 feet a year. In East Anglia the cliff between Cromer and Mundesley, made partly of Tertiary beds, but mainly of glacial deposits, receded 330 feet between 1838 and 1861— i.e., 14 feet per annum—and 840 feet between 1861 and 1905—i.e., 19 feet per annum. Along the East Anglian coast several old villages have disappeared, their sites now being entirely covered by the sea.

The coast of East Yorkshire between Flamborough Head and Spurn Point is made up mainly of boulder clay, and has been subject to intensive erosion from coastal and tidal currents. The rate can be estimated in this part for a very long period. From abundant evidence it is calculated that the coast in the period of Roman occupation lay on an average 3½ miles to the seaward of its present line. A number of ancient villages have been lost by the encroachment of the sea. The rate has been over 7 feet per year for many centuries. In the period since the first Ordnance Survey of the coast was completed the rate of erosion has

been proved to be 5 feet 6 inches a year. One example
of the kind of records available can be taken in Old Kilnsea
Church. In 1776 the church was 95 yards inland from the
sea, but a report by Smeaton, the engineer, a few years earlier
estimated the inroads of the sea at about 10 yards a year.
In 1786 the sea had reached the churchyard wall, and the
east end of the chancel was then 12 yards from the cliff
edge. In 1793 the chancel was undermined, and in 1799
the nave was destroyed. In 1805 the tower at the west
end of the church was still 22 yards from the cliff, 8 yards
from the cliff in 1814, and disappeared in 1816. In 1833
its foundations were 17 yards seaward. In 1899 it was
visited at a specially low tide, at 250 yards seaward from
the cliff edge. The process of coastal erosion thus presents a
serious problem, and the efforts to control and check it
will be discussed in a later chapter.

Coastal Accretion.

It has been made clear in the discussion of all forms of
erosion that the eroded material is transported either by
wind or water to some other area and re-deposited. The
wind-blown dust either falls into the sea and lakes, or is
accumulated on land areas as loess, while all streams and
rivers carry vast loads of rock detritus to the sea. This,
together with the material won from the land by marine
erosion, is eventually deposited either along the coast
or in the sea itself. We will examine first what becomes of
much of the material removed from parts of the coast by
the varied action of the sea.

As the waves generated by the tides only strike the coastline at right angles in rare conditions, but mostly impinge
with the line of their crest at an angle to the line of the
beach, the rush of water following the breaking of a wave is
usually up the beach at an angle to the perpendicular,
and the scour or run-back of the wave is at a corresponding
angle, the other side of the perpendicular. In other words,
the water which rushes up the beach from one spot runs
back into the sea at a point farther along shore in the direction

of the travel of the wave. The beach material that is
rolled back and forth by the waves thus traverses a series
of looped or V-shaped paths with the point of the V turned
inland. In this way the aggregate movement of the beach
pebbles is along shore in the direction of the shore current.
Along the east coast of England this direction is generally
southward, so that there is a constant southward drift of
material along the shore. Where such a shoreline drift
comes against the mouth of a river with its strong river
current setting out to sea, there is a conflict of currents
and an area of quieter water where much of the material
is dropped to form a sand or gravel bank. The first accumulation of such a bank will in turn react on the currents,
and from place to place along the coast conditions are
established where the coastal drift material is allowed
to accumulate. During all this action, of course, much of
the finer detritus produced by the abrasion and the mud
washed from clay cliffs and brought down by rivers are
carried out to sea and deposited away from the land.
While the areas of coastal accumulation do not balance
the areas of erosion, they are none the less of some importance. At the southern end of the area of erosion
just described in east Yorkshire, the large volume and
current of the Humber meeting the coastwise currents
produce eddy water in which gravel ridges and banks have
for long been building up. These are, however, not
permanent because, as they move and extend southward
across the river mouth they restrict the river channel and
so increase the velocity and cutting power of the water
sufficiently to remove them again. There is thus an area
around Spurn Point of unstable balance between erosion
and accumulation. In East Anglia there are areas where
accumulation has definitely exceeded erosion and new land
has been built up. The River Alde, which now enters the
sea south of Orford Ness, is a case in point. The river,
flowing eastward, approaches within 50 yards of the
sea, just south of the town of Aldeburgh, then, turning
south, runs for about 8 miles down the coast, separated
from the sea by high gravel ridges, which have been piled

up in the course of centuries. The ridge formed originally at the mouth of the river near Aldeburgh has gradually extended south at a greater rate than the river could cope with. In the twelfth century Orford Castle was built to guard what was then the mouth of the river, but the growth of the gravel bank has left it by now $5\frac{1}{2}$ miles up the river. In 700 years the gravel bank has extended to the south a distance of $5\frac{1}{2}$ miles—that is, about 13 to 14 yards a year. Opposite Orford the gravel is built out into a prominent point—Orford Ness—where the shore current takes a more south-westerly direction.

Farther south the great area of Romney Marsh has been built up from the sea by the deposition of gravel in a former sheltered embayment of the coast. This area is backed by cliffs of Cretaceous rocks, while the coast north of Hythe is of softer materials which provide abundant material for coastal drifting. This is dropped in the comparatively quiet area of the old bay, and the coastal currents through many centuries have shaped it into its present unstable form. The ridges are not permanent, as great changes have taken place during historic time, and the position of the prominence of Dungeness itself is at present moving eastward and extending farther seaward, while its southern side is being slowly reduced.

A common process in the coastal accumulation is first the formation of a long strip of gravel flanking the shore, which strip will be emphasised by occasional storm-beach material piled upon it. This gravel bank impedes drainage from the land, and often either salt marshes or swamps are formed on the landward side. In time these silt up and an area of land is made where formerly was only sea. The gravel is added to, and if conditions become at all stable, then large areas of land may be built up or, alternatively, unstable areas of shifting gravel banks will be produced. It is one of the many problems shared by geologist and civil engineer to endeavour to stabilise some of these areas of coastal accretion and render the added land usable and permanent.

Deltaic Deposition.

The deposits formed where a river enters the sea most frequently take the form of a sand-bar or a sand and gravel spit stretching across the river mouth, or elongating itself out from the shore in a slant across the main river current. This formation is the result of the rapid slackening of the river current as its water mingles with the vastly greater volume of the sea, the current thus being slowed to such an extent that it can no longer carry the coarser-grade material that is being rolled and carried along its channel. While fresh water can carry a great load of fine mud in suspension, the salt water of the sea has the effect of flocculating and precipitating much of this, so that at the zone of mixing of the waters a considerable amount of mud is added to the sand-bar. Storms from the sea tend to move the accumulated bar up into the mouth of the river and river-floods tend to move it farther seawards. Between these two forces the bar remains as a moving and ever-changing obstruction, being constantly worn and eroded by tide and storm, but constantly renewed by the deposit of fresh material from the river. This changeableness of a river-bar makes a great part of its danger to shipping and constitutes a serious problem in its control.

When a river enters a nearly tideless sea or an area of coast where currents are weak or absent, the accumulation may proceed unchecked, and a large area of silt and sandy deposit is built out into the sea, usually achieving a triangular shape, from which the Greeks gave such accumulation the name of delta, from the shape of the Greek letter $D = \Delta$.

In the conditions which allow of the formation of a delta, the river arriving at the sea drops its coarser material in the estuary or widened mouth of the river, and the current spreads out wider and shallower to pass over the bar so formed. Finer sediment that can still be carried by the slowed-down current is thus carried forward and spread across a wider front as the current dies away in the sea. In a short time parts of the bar near the edge of the river current build up nearly to the surface level of the water, and in times of low water first salt-marsh plants, and later reeds and other vegetation, get a footing on the surface. In times of flood the vegetation breaks the current, and more material is deposited among its stems, thus making its position secure. As the deltaic surface is thus built up, the river is again partially confined to a narrower channel and carries its detritus farther forward, tipping it over a widening seaward front. In flood-waters the river breaks out in branching channels across the accumulating delta surface, and we get the opposite of the conditions which pertain to the river valley. There the river is augmented by the constant confluence of tributaries, but as the delta grows in area, the main river channel is constantly depleted by the breaking away of subsidiary channels or ' distributaries ' which wander across the delta flats to the sea. The break-up of the main current by distributaries helps the deposition of sediment and carries much of it to the sides of the delta. Hence a delta always tends to grow forward into the sea and at the same time to widen out sideways as it does so, thus producing the triangle of new land with its apex up the river and its curved front or base in the sea. The building up of the surface of the delta that is hastened by the growth of vegetation, and in turn gives fresh land for such growth, proceeds more quickly on the older part or inland end of the delta than it does on the new and forward edge and in consequence the inland end or apex is rapidly raised above the sea level. The surface of a delta therefore closely approximates to a very flat cone with its apex or point in the river mouth and its convex base sticking out into the sea. Over this surface there will be one or two main river channels and a host of smaller and intermittent distributaries, some operative only during river-floods. The main channels will continue to build out rapidly into the sea, their material forming bars and spits that gradually meet and cut off a lagoon or swamp elongated along the front of the delta. The distributaries will proceed to build small deltas in these lagoons, and soon fill them up. It is sometimes possible to improve one of the main channels across a delta, by canalising it, to carry its current well out to sea by building piers or levees to carry it beyond the immediate beach currents, and so ensure that its current remains steady and strong. If this can be accomplished, then that channel has a good chance of remaining free from deposition and can be kept open for shipping; if this is not done, then the channels, left to themselves, are liable to sudden changes in storms, to constant shifting and to rapid variation in depth and are most difficult for navigation. This control of delta channels has been carried to a fine art in the Mississippi, Nile, and Ganges deltas particularly. In the case of the Mississippi, the concentration upon one main channel has focused the forward building of the delta around that, and the lateral distributaries have built up large coastal swamps and a considerable area of ground just below sea level, so that the main channel is over a very narrow ' dry ' ridge across an area of very shallow sea, over the slightly submerged main delta surface. During flood periods, when the river overflows its banks, silt is deposited and most abundantly immediately adjacent to the stream and along the bottom of the channel. In this way after repeated flooding a natural levee or bank is raised and the river runs on ground that is slightly higher than the flood-plain around it. This enables new distributaries to break out at many places, and contributes to the rapid changes in the delta topography. The first distributory leaves the main river at about 200 miles distance from the Gulf of Mexico, and the area of the delta is about 12,300 square miles. The advance of the delta front into the Gulf of Mexico is about 260 feet a year (Fig. 4).

Some of the finer sediment carried down by rivers is carried beyond the delta to the sea and from the shore outwards there is a zone of deposition of fine mud of varying width. If a section were taken through a delta or any shore-line deposit and continued seaward, we should find the sediments grading from the coarsest near the shore to fine sand, then to coarse mud, to finer muds, and finally to the finest oozes, as we progress from shallow to deep water. In the delta the deposition has certain structural features

that result from the mode of formation. We can regard
the river current as carrying debris to the edge of the delta

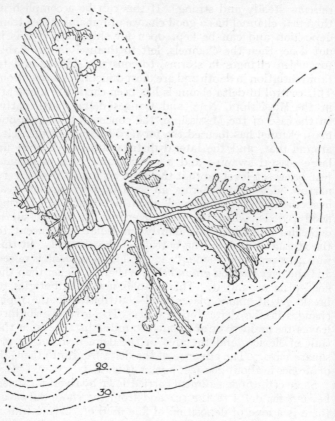

FIG. 4.—Delta of Mississippi.

Showing exposed area (shaded), topset beds (dotted), and steep
front. Contours are depth of water in fathoms.

and there dropping it, to roll down the steeper front and to
the sea floor. The deposition resembles closely the tipping

of an embankment where the bank grows by constant accession to the forward slope. All the time the delta is building thin deposits are being added to the top surface, forming what are called the ' top-set ' beds—these have finer silts deposited after flood-times—as the commoner constituent. The debris carried to the forward edge builds up a slope at the angle of rest, and down the slope the coarser pebbles and sands tend to roll, to accumulate at the bottom, so that we get ' fore-set ' beds with a skirt or footing of pebbles and sand. Over the footing, and extending forward of the delta along the sea floor, we get the finer muds becoming finer and finer grained as we pass farther seaward. The ' bedding ' or layering of a typical delta is thus peculiar. Any individual sheet of material deposited during a short period has a long, slightly sloping topset part, a short, steeper foreset bed with coarse, pebbly footing to it, and a long, forward apron of finer mud. The whole delta will form a lens of deposits with a tapering edge at the landward and seaward ends, and within the lens or lenticle there is abundant ' cross-bedding ' or ' current-bedding '—the steep-sloping foreset beds. The bottom of the delta beds tends to be marked by the accumulated pebble beds or ' conglomerates ' rolled down the forward slope. These characters can be recognised in many of the coarser sandstones of many geological ages—the Millstone Grit series of Carboniferous age, which occur in most parts of the Pennines and parts of Wales and the borders, contains many sandstone beds that thin out into shale when traced in one direction and which when seen in vertical section exhibit perfect ' current-bedding ' with pebble beds, topset beds, and all the other characters of delta deposits (Fig. 5).

In a typical extensive delta vegetation grows out over parts of the surface, and in times of flooding, or with settlement of the accumulating debris, such vegetation may be overwhelmed with silt or mud and be incorporated in the material of the delta. Most deltas accumulate in areas where the sea-floor is gradually sinking, so that successive surfaces are overgrown, then submerged and eventually the delta incorporates within its substance many layers of vegetable remains, peaty material, and some animal remains. These in time change to layers of coaly substance with many fossils in them. It is briefly in this way that the Coal Measures accumulated. Large deltaic and estuarine areas of swamp and peaty bogs were incorporated in floods of deltaic debris, which in course of time have provided the material of the coal strata (see Chapter XV).

Wherever a river brings debris to the sea there is this marked outward zoning of the material deposited—coarse, sandy stuff near the shore, passing outward through finer

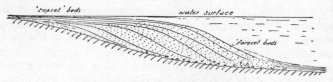

FIG. 5.—Section of a Simple Delta.

sands to coarse muds, then through finer muds to the fine oozes of the areas where detritus scarcely reaches. These oozes are mostly made of the calcareous parts of sea creatures, the almost microscopic foramenifera, shell-fish of all kinds, corals and other animals, and also microscopic simple plants, diatoms, etc., which make a skeleton by extracting lime or silica from the sea-water. The hard parts sink to the sea-floor, along with a small quantity of the finest wind-blown dust, and form an essentially calcareous ooze. When these different zoned materials are indurated to form rocks we get our main sedimentary groups, coarse sandstones, flagstones where the sands and finer muds alternate, shales from the mud zone, and limestone from the oozes. In areas where the sea-floor is unstable and is either rising or sinking there is a recognisable succession of deposits which enable the direction of movement to be determined from the rocks formed and their relation to one another. If we take the case of a sea-floor sinking, the deltas forming in that sea will be gradually drowned. The sea will at successive stages enter farther into the mouth of the river, and the zones of deposition will in effect move inland as the seashore encroaches upon the land. Where the first coarse zone occupied the shore-line in the first stage of the sea by sinking of the sea-floor and rise of sea-level relative to the land, this at a later stage will be under deeper water, with the new coarse deposit zone now forming over what before had been the land coastal strip, and the finer mud zone will now occupy the area formerly occupied by sandy deposition. The calcareous oozes will also now be dropped over the earlier mud-zone. As sinking proceeds there may be still further shifting of the zones, so that limestones will form over mudstones and mudstones over sandstones, and the sandstone on what was formerly dry land. This condition is called a ' marine transgression ', the sea gradually encroaching on the land. After a period of such transgression, a vertical section through the delta would show a typical change from bottom to top, the beds being arranged roughly as follows:

Coarse sandstone-sandstone-shale-limestone.
Coarse sandstone-sandstone-shale-limestone.
Coarse sandstone-sandstone-shale-limestone.

To the left of this series we should find coarse sandstones and conglomerates overlying and ' overstepping ' the older rocks which formed the land surface, while in the mid-delta area we should have a vertical succession from sandstones at the bottom through shales to limestones at the top. If we consider an area where the sea is lowering, or, alternatively, where the land area is rising, the opposite will be the case. The zones of deposition and the delta front will move progressively seaward and the opposite vertical succession will result.

Coarse sandstones
Sandstones
Shales
Limestones.

Where we meet such a superposition of rocks accompanied by marked current bedding in the sandstones and traces of topset and foreset beds, we have strong evidence of the past existence of deltaic conditions over that area when the rocks were forming. In this way we can apply Lyell's doctrine and can interpret the geological past in terms of present processes, looking for the characters of a modern delta preserved in ancient rock formations.

Over the greater part of the sea-floor where sedimentation is taking place slowly by accumulation of mud and ooze the layers deposited are of such wide extent that they take on the character of thin sheets, to all intents and purposes laid down in nearly horizontal layers one over the other. It is only near the coastline and in the locally thicker deposits of deltas that this comparison does not hold closely enough for all practical purposes. If the movement of land relative to sea consisted only of a vertical one of elevation, bringing these beds in their undisturbed state above sea-level, we should find everywhere only approximately horizontal strata of very wide extent. There are a few areas where such has been the main movement and where we now have beds of material deposited in the seas of past geological periods, now forming the land surface for thousands of square miles. In parts of the Russian and Siberian plains, as in parts of the prairie areas of North America, the same strata occupy the surface of the ground for scores or hundreds of miles, everywhere nearly horizontal. Had that been the case everywhere, we should have very little knowledge of the rocks of the earth's crust beyond those formed in the more recent periods. Fortunately for geological investigators, many parts of the earth's crust have been subjected to pressures and movements which have bent and folded strata, broken them, and moved parts to great distances up or down, so that in some part of the world even the oldest and first-formed sediments have been elevated to great heights, subjected to denudation and erosion, and so exposed for our study. The structures of folds, faults, and the movements that have exposed the older as well as the newer beds at the surface will be the subject of the next chapter.

CHAPTER IV

Rock structures. Bedding. Joints. Inclination—dip, strike. Folding —anticlines, synclines, mountain folds. Dislocations—faults, trough faulting, etc.; fault systems. Metamorphism—cleavage.

Bedding.

THE great majority of the sediments deposited in water, and many of those that accumulate on land, are deposited in more or less regular layers, often with a change of character or composition from one layer to another. When such deposits are indurated (hardened) or consolidated by the addition of cementing material between their grains, the individual layers remain clearly defined as separate strata and the rock is said to be stratified. When such a stratified rock is exposed to weathering there are certain planes within it along which weathering soon effects a division in the rock and along which the rock is more easily split than in another direction. Such divisional planes are called ' bedding ' when parallel to the floor on which they were deposited, and ' joints ' when at right angles to, or highly inclined to the beddidg. The bedding is usually of very wide extent, the bedding planes being traceable over most of the lateral extent of a stratum, while the joints are much shorter, limited to the thickness of an individual ' bed ' or layer. Sedimentary strata vary in the thickness of the individual bed from less than an inch in fine shales to an extreme thickness of many feet, possibly as much as 100 feet or more, in the extreme case of some sandstones. In nearly all rocks the average thickness of the separate strata—that is, the vertical distance between the bedding planes—is only a matter of a few feet.

Within a stratum—that is, between two adjacent bedding planes—there may be finer horizontal divisions, or laminæ, along which the rock will split. This is seen in shales which will often break off from an outcrop in thin beds, which in turn can be split off, with care, in thin laminæ.

There is usually some difference, either slight or possibly very marked, between adjacent beds, but the laminæ within one bed have all the same character. In the discussion of delta formation it was explained that there is frequently some current bedding present. This is a common feature of most coarse sandstones. The sand being rolled and moved along the bottom of a current of water is piled up in irregular banks and tipped over the front of accumulated heaps, so that the stratum of sand, while keeping approximately a parallel top and bottom layer which become the main bedding planes, has the cross layers within. The parallel beds define the stratum, the layers between the current bedding being lenticles or laminæ.

The surface of sandstones that have been deposited near the shore-line often carry evidence of this in the form of ripple markings. The separate laminæ or the thinner strata have been laid down as sand between tide-marks, and their surface has been moulded into sand-ripples like those on any modern shore. The next tide in some cases has spread either mud or fine sand over them without destroying the rippling. On consolidation, the ripples are thus perfectly preserved in the sandstone, and the overlying stratum will carry a cast of them. This preservation of surface texture is often surprisingly complete in shales or marls that have originated in lake or land areas, where the mud of a lake-floor has been exposed by partial drying up. In these muds the commonest effect is that produced by the drying, which causes the mud to crack in a polygonal system, such as can be seen in a dry summer along the margins of a reservoir. Footprints of animals may also be left in the sand or mud and the curious and distinctive trails made by certain shell-fish, by worms and other creatures. No opportunity of examining freshly opened bedding planes should be neglected, and a sharp look-out must be kept for such striking evidence of the actual conditions of deposition of the rocks. Such markings are evidence of ' littoral ' or ' shore-line ' deposition, or possibly of deposition in temporary lakes in an area of desert climate. In the latter case the sun-cracks in the marl are often filled with wind-blown sand, having the characteristic desert polish, and the marls may carry deep rain-pittings, the effect of some violent temporary storm. Studied in conjunction with the plant remains that may be fossilised in the rocks, such evidence enables us to reconstruct past geological climates with some degree of certainty.

In many series of rocks the strata are seen to change in character from one bed to another, through a limited range, and the changes are repeated time after time. This repetition of a particular grouping is called ' rhythmic deposition ', and is clearly seen in many of the Carboniferous and Jurassic rocks in this country. In the Yoredale series, for instance, in the Lower Carboniferous, there are great thicknesses of strata exposed in Derbyshire and through most of the Pennines, where any deep section will show a constant repetition of limestone, shale, sandstone, limestone, shale, sandstone, through hundreds of feet, although the individual beds may be only a few feet thick. This succession of the three dominant types of sedimentary rocks constantly repeated is a very widespread phenomenon and its origin is still a matter of research and discussion.

In shales it is quite frequently found that there are certain levels at which a thin stratum of unusual character occurs. This will consist of a definite layer along which a different rock occurs in rounded spheroids: masses which are oval or circular in plan, and flattened oval in section—these are ' concretions '. The most common concretionary rocks are the ' clay ironstones ' and other calcareous materials. They have been deposited usually as the result of chemical precipitation, or have drawn together in concretionary form as a result of chemical action taking place while the whole mass of the stratum was in liquid mud condition. When a concretionary layer is thick the concretions may coalesce and form a definite stratum with its ' bedding planes ' irregular and made up of the curves of the successive concretions. As many concretions are started by the presence of a concentration of organic acid disturbing the chemical balance, and the commonest source of such acid is found in the decay of an animal or plant, it is often found that the actual concretion has formed around a fragment of plant or animal that is preserved as a fossil at the core. It is worth while spending some time acquiring the ' knack ' of splitting concretions along their central horizontal plane, as, when fossils do occur, they are often surprisingly complete in their preservation. In the Coal Measure shales the ironstone concretions have yielded amazing quantities of the fruit-cones of trees, of fish-scales, even of complete fishes, and of insects ancestral to the dragon-flies, of small crab-like creatures, and a fine selection of the so-called ' ferns '. Concretions in the Lias shales and in the Jurassic strata frequently contain ammonites, occasion-ally so well preserved as to retain some trace of the colouring of the shells. A very sharp blow with a light hammer is the only way to crack a concretion successfully, and the blow should be given at the narrow end, not on any of the broader faces.

Joints.

In addition to the bedding, most sedimentary rocks are traversed by a second set of divisional planes at right angles or highly inclined to the bedding; these are called ' joints '. The jointing often varies in its sharpness and the spacing between successive joints, roughly in proportion to the fineness of the rock constituents. Coarse sandstones sometimes have the joints a few feet or even a yard or two apart. When this occurs in thick bedded sandstone it can be quarried in large masses for structural purposes and has a high commercial value. In very fine-grained rock the joints are very clean-cut and may be so fine as to be in-visible in the unweathered rock. This is the case in most limestones, but the attack of frost and rain or a blow from the hammer will soon reveal the jointing. There are usually two sets of vertical joints, which may themselves be at right angles or approaching that position, thus causing sedimen-tary rocks to split up into approximate cubes or rectangular blocks when weathered or quarried.

The cause of jointing is somewhat obscure, but much of it is probably due to one or both of two causes. On drying out, a sedimentary rock will undergo a certain amount of contraction, and the formation of joints allows the horizontal component of this contraction to act, while the vertical contraction takes place under pressure, and so produces a compacting of the rock and not a tension. When rocks have hardened and become brittle, any torsional strain due to the tilting or irregular bending of a large area of country may induce a set of joints, just as similar sets of cracks at right angles to one another are produced in a sheet of glass that is twisted. The two effects of contraction and torsion probably supplement one another, and it is almost impossible to separate them.

In igneous rocks there is no bedding within a main mass, and the jointing, due to contraction on cooling, is usually irregular. In the case of some rocks, however, and particularly in basalts, the jointing formed by contraction has a very regular pattern, splitting the rock up into vertical hexagonal columns, often of striking regularity. Such jointing is familiar to everyone in the pictures of the Giant's Causeway in Northern Ireland, or the cliffs of the island of Staffa, both in rocks of basaltic composition.

Inclination of Rocks.

At many periods in the history of the earth different parts of its outer crust have been subjected to stresses which have resulted in the movement of sections of the crust and the rucking up or folding of parts of its outer layers. The regions in which the folding is most intense are usually those where sedimentation has been taking place and where there are deep deposits of soft or partially consolidated material. The movement resembles the crumpling of a thin sheet of flexible material held edge-on between the jaws of a slow-moving vice, one jaw fixed and the other moving up towards it. In the case of Europe and Africa, it can be shown geologically that the main mass of older rocks in the present African continent have in a past geological period moved northward, crushing together the soft sediments that had accumulated to the north over an area of which the present Mediterranean Sea is only a small remnant, and folding them up into the Alps and other mountain ranges against the old rocks of the north European continent. In general, the newer mountain ranges and areas of folded rocks are piled up against the edges of the vast plains of ancient crystalline rocks, the Archæan shields, already described.

When the whole area of folding is examined, the pattern of the folds is similar to that which would occur if a cloth on a table were loaded at one part and then pushed up against that load from a distant point. The cloth would ruck up into high ridges against the fixed load, and into less sharp ridges against the hands that were pushing, but between those two parts would be a broad area of shallower folds. Against the fixed load the ridges would be high and narrow, and the folds might be sufficiently sharp and high to become top-heavy and they would then fall forward in the direction of the push, forming an ' overfold '. Behind that there is generally a belt of ' normal folds ' where the folds are like waves, fairly regular and even ; the greater part of the area will, however, be occupied by very ' flat ' folds, gentle undulations where the height of the fold is very small compared with the width from crest to crest, the ' amplitude '. In this area of very gentle folding there is a great expanse of rock between crest and trough of each fold, where the ' flank ' of the fold has a fairly constant slope, possibly for miles in extent.

If large masses of country are gently tilted, all the constituent rocks that may originally have been horizontal will be gently inclined. It is not easy, nor is it often possible in a restricted area to tell whether a patch of rocks that are inclined from the horizontal belong to part of a flat fold, or are just part of a general tilted area. This can only be decided by careful mapping and by following the rocks for a considerable distance to see how the tilt terminates. In either case the immediate effect is the same: the rocks have a slope from the horizontal and the maximum slope direction is called the direction of ' dip ' and the variation from the horizontal is the amount of the dip. In all notes of the field examination of rocks, the dip with its direction and amount is an essential feature to be noted, as changes in the amount and direction of the dip will give the evidence and nature of any folding that is present. If a line is taken on a rock surface at right angles to the dip, this will be seen to be horizontal, and this is called the ' strike ' of the rock. In a level country of great plains the ' strike ' will coincide

FIG. 6.—Strike and Dip in Inclined Strata.

with the outcrop of a stratum, but where the surface is not level, then strike and outcrop are different (Fig. 6).

Great care must be exercised in securing a measure of the dip in a section, such as a quarry. If the face of the quarry in which the rock is exposed is cut parallel to the dip, then of course the ' true dip '—that is, the maximum slope —will be seen. If the quarry face is cut at right angles to the dip, only the ' strike section ' of the rocks is visible, and that will show the bedding planes of the rocks as horizontal, the strike line always being horizontal. At any intermediate angle something between these two extremes will be visible, and that we call an ' apparent

dip '. In any exposure, if a bedding plane is seen anywhere well exposed, then the dip or strike or both can be
easily measured; but if not, then at least *two* sections must
be seen and the apparent dips recorded, as the true dip
can be calculated from two such records.

In most cases it is found that inclined strata can be
treated as the flanks of a fold. If followed far enough, the
dip will begin to change as either the crest or trough of a fold
is approached. If we start on a stratum with a dip which
is ' strong '—say 30 or 40 degrees or more—and walk
' against the direction of dip '—that is, up the slope—if
we are on the flanks of a fold then the dip will soon begin to
decrease and will pass by gradual change to a horizontal
position of no dip; passing this point, the dip will be seen
to be in the opposite direction, and we shall begin to walk
down the slope, or ' with the dip ', at an increasing slope
as we go forward. After a time the dip would reach a
nearly constant value and so long as it remained at that
value we should be on rocks with ' uniform dip '. The dip
would next change in the opposite way—that is, in continuing down the slope, the dip would slacken, and by gradual
decrease reach zero again, with the rocks horizontal;
passing that point, we should then begin to climb *up* an
increasing dip, to another patch of uniform dip similar to
the one on which we started. In that little walk we should
have passed across two complete folds, first an upfold, or
arch, and then over a downfold or trough. These two folds
are called respectively an **anticline**, the upfold, and a
syncline, the downfold. Now, it will be seen that between
the anticline and syncline we walked over an area of
uniformly dipping rocks, the dip being the maximum
for that area, which we could describe either as the ' flank '
or side of the anticline as we came down from the crest of
that first fold, or equally well as the flank of the syncline as
we went down towards its trough. It is inevitable that
wherever rocks are folded, in the majority of cases anticline and syncline will follow one another and between them
will be areas of dipping strata that form the common flank
to both folds. We should expect, then, when an area of

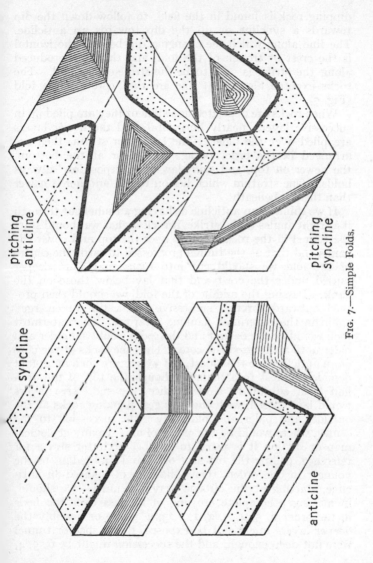

pitching anticline

pitching syncline

syncline

anticline

Fig. 7.—Simple Folds.

dipping rock is found in the field, to follow down the dip towards a syncline or up the dip towards an anticline. The line along which the changing dip becomes horizontal is the crest or trough of the fold, and that line produced along the strike is said to be the strike of the fold. The rocks exposed along that line are the ' core ' of the fold (Fig. 7).

When rocks are deposited as sediment they are piled up in successive layers, nearly horizontal, and the newer layers are piled over the older. The layers, or strata, then are arranged in the order of age, the older at the bottom, the newer on top, and this ' law of superposition ' always holds. One stratum which lies on top of another is newer than the one beneath.

If we think of an anticline as having a tunnel cut through it at right angles to the strike, it is clear that we should start the tunnel in the rocks that go over the top and cover the flanks and that as the tunnel progressed towards the centre of the fold we should cut into rocks that were deeper buried under the crest and that lay below those on the flank. Passing the middle of the fold, we should then proceed outward through successive strata till we emerged again in the outermost flanking stratum. The outermost rock would be the newest and the rocks would get older and older until we crossed the core. Thus the rocks at the core of an anticline are the oldest. If we picture such an upfold denuded almost to a plain as though the top of the arch had been cut off in a clean slice, the successive layers would be exposed, with the youngest flanking rocks at the outside, and older and older layers in succession to the centre, where would be the oldest of all. In any geological map or section it is usual to number or letter strata for reference, calling the oldest 1 or a, and proceeding to the younger in due order. On a diagram of a sliced-off anticline, starting at the outside—say stratum 6—we should, in making a complete crossing of it, pass over the beds in the order 6, 5, 4, 3, 2, 1, 2, 3, 4, 5, 6; or possibly the deeper layers might not be exposed, if the slice or tunnel were not deep enough, and the succession might be 6, 5, 4,

3, 4, 5, 6. In all cases the succession would be from younger to older and back to younger rocks. It is in this way that anticlines are recognised in the field, either by this succession of strata when travelling at right angles to the strike, or by the changing dips.

In the case of a syncline the opposite arrangement of strata is the case. The dip, followed down the flank of the fold, becomes less until it becomes zero, then increases again ; but while in the anticline the direction of the dips was outward down the flanks, away from the core of the fold, in the syncline it is inward into the trough. The strata in a syncline have sunk (a simple mnemonic to remember the folds is anticlines are arched, synclines have sunk) and so the younger rocks will be folded into the top of the depression and the older rocks will be deep down in the fold. Passing from the flanks across the fold we should have the opposite case to the anticline and the strata would be met in the order 1, 2, 3, 4, 5, 6, 5, 4, 3, 2, 1, or perhaps 2, 3, 4, 5, 4, 3, 2, etc.

On the surface such a sliced-off fold, either anticline or syncline, would show as parallel outcrops of rock symmetrically arranged about the core or ' axis ' of the fold, if the dip were the same on each flank. In many cases, however, the fold is steeper on one flank than on the other and is described as an asymmetric fold. On a level section the outcrops would then be wider on the side with gentle dip and narrower on the steep flank, but still parallel, if the axis were horizontal. Suppose an anticlinal fold is made in stiff paper (do this for yourself) and the arch stood on a table so that the crest of the fold is parallel to the table-top and is horizontal. The axis of the fold is then horizontal, but if the fold is tilted by one end, so that the crest and axis have a dip as well as the flanks, then the fold is said to ' pitch '. A strike line is *always* horizontal, and if a horizontal line is now drawn on the side of the fold it will soon pass round the nose of the fold and along the other flank, and will actually be a rounded V shape, a parabola—so if the top of the fold were cut off by a horizontal plane, the outcrops of all the beds would be parabolas. The curve

C—GEOL.

would be closed at the point where it crossed the nose of the anticline, and would widen out as it passed back along the flanks, in the direction opposite to the dip. In the case of a syncline, the section of the strata in a similar way would make parabolic curves, but they would open out in the same direction as the dip. In the case of pitching folds, therefore, the outcrop widens *against* the dip in an anticline and *with* the dip in a syncline and in both cases is roughly V-shaped. These generalisations are useful when looking at a geological map, as folds are often at once apparent by this V-shaping of an outcrop, and then either the relative age of the beds or the direction of the dips will tell at once the nature of the fold.

Folds are often clearly revealed as the result of weathering. When an anticline is formed, the rocks on the outer layers of the arch are stretched, joints are opened, and ' tension cracks ' are made, so that the whole texture of rock on the outer part of the crest is open and offers all facilities for the penetration of weathering agents. Frost and water have free entry to considerable depth and streams find the ground ready broken and loosened. As a result of these factors, anticlines often weather out into valleys. In the core of a syncline the rocks are considerably compressed, the joints closed up, and the whole texture solidified, so that weathering agents have less access and synclines resist denudation. This is confirmed by the very common synclinal structure of hills. In addition to the access to weathering so afforded, a hill with a synclinal structure is far more stable and less liable to landslipping than one which is anticlinal. If the strata dips outwards (an anticlinal hill), then the lubrication as rain penetrates along the bedding planes helps the formation of giant landslips, and the hill is soon reduced. In a synclinal hill the pull of gravity is down the dip slope as the bedding planes are lubricated, and that is into the hillside, so that landslips are extremely rare with this structure.

In large-scale folding it is often the case that an asymmetric anticline has one limb very nearly vertical and the other only slightly inclined. This special case is

usually called a ' monocline ', and very often, when traced
for some distance laterally, a monocline is found passing
into a normal fault.   Much of the western edge of the
Pennines is of this monoclinal structure, the dip of the rocks
being very steep towards the Lancashire and Cheshire
plains and very gentle towards the east.   When a monocline is deeply eroded there may be exposed a narrow belt of
vertical rocks along the steep limb, such as that which
runs across the Isle of Wight from east to west, and can be
seen in section in Alum Bay and other places around the
coast.

Dislocations of Strata.

The folding of rocks that has just been described is
achieved in response to forces of compression acting over a
fairly wide area of the earth's surface.   In contrast with
these forces are those of tension, tending to stretch part of
the crust, and these forces produce the structures called
faults of normal type.   The type of fault or fracture of the
crust called ' reverse ' faulting is produced in extreme
cases of folding.   It was mentioned that anticlines and
synclines are often asymmetric, with a steeper limb on the
forward side, in the direction of the push which creates
the folds.   If the push continues, the fold, in the case of an
anticline, may become very high and top-heavy, and fall
over in the forward direction, producing an overturned or
' recumbent ' fold.   In the case where the rocks of the limb
of the anticline are not such as will yield easily to the
stretching and distortion that accompany folding of an
extreme nature, the rocks may shear instead of bending,
and the top of the fold is then thrust over the underlying
limb, along a shear plane that is inclined to the horizontal.
This is called a thrust plane when the angle to the horizontal
is small and the ' travel ' of the upper rocks is large, but
when the plane of dislocation is highly inclined to the
horizontal and the push of the upper rocks has not carried
them far beyond the same rocks in the lower limb, then we
have a ' reversed fault '.

The faulting that is produced in areas of tension is simpler. A block of country being stretched will fail along one or more lines and a slab of ' country rock ' on one side of the ' fault ' slips down relative to the other side. If a particular stratum, say a coal seam, is followed on one side of a fault, in a direction approaching the fault at right angles, the miner will come to a line across his workings where the coal seam is cut off at a straight line—that is, the fault face. On crossing this line, which is usually a narrow belt of broken rock and clay rubbish, from a few inches to a few feet thick, and mining forward at the same level, he will find his workings lying in an entirely different stratum from that on the other side of the fault. By the consideration of these new strata he will decide whether they belong higher or lower in the local series of rocks than the coal-seam he was working. Suppose them to be higher—that is, younger rocks. He will then begin to mine downwards through them until he reaches the coal-seam at some lower level and can then mine forward in the coal-seam, exactly as before the fault intervened. If the strata have a dip on the first side of the fault, then that dip will be continued in the seam in its new position across the fault. The amount the miner has to descend vertically, from the position of the coal one side of the fault to its new level on the other, is the ' throw ' of the fault—that is, the amount of vertical displacement of any stratum along that fault line. The fault plane is never quite vertical itself, but is inclined to the vertical and dips down steeply towards the low side of the fault. The low side is called the ' downthrow side ', and the high side is the ' upthrow side '. The angle that the fault plane makes with the *vertical* is called the ' hade ' of the fault, and commonly this is about 15 degrees. As the strata ends have moved apart down this inclined plane, there will be a horizontal displacement, as well as a vertical, between them. This horiontal displacement is the ' gape ' or ' want ' of the fault, and in coal-mining it may represent the loss of a large area of coal within a colliery lease, if the fault is large. On approaching a fault, the strata are generally found to be broken and bent within a few feet of the actual break, suggesting that they first began to bend before the final dislocation took place. A fault like this just described is called a 'normal fault'. If the miner continued through the fault, making his tunnel at the level of the coal on the upthrow side, he would find himself working in newer strata on the downthrow side, with the coal sunk beneath him to the depth of the throw. At the surface, where a fault crosses a piece of country and the effect of erosion has been to level off the surface, the same rule will apply—on the downthrow side of the fault newer strata are brought to the same level as older strata on the upthrow side. This is often the first indication of a fault in field-mapping, when there is a jump in age from older to younger or younger to older strata across a particular line. The throw can be determined if the age and succession of the rocks are known in detail, even if the fault is never seen in section.

A fault cannot extend forever, in either direction horizontally, and sooner or later it dies out; consequently, on a large area, the throw of a fault will usually be found to change from place to place, the change being gradual. Faults only very rarely occur in isolation—that is, in single examples. Where an area is subject to tension it is usual for a whole pattern of faults to be formed, sometimes not unlike the joint patterns in rocks. The 'major' faults will usually be in one direction, and may form great belts of closely set or branching faults, with 'minor' faults either at right angles to them or inclined at an angle across them. Faults are of many different ages, and sometimes a pattern has developed at two different periods. In that case the newer faults may cut the older set and fault them just as strata are faulted. In inclined rocks, if the fault does not coincide exactly with the strike of the strata, then there will be some amount of horizontal displacement of outcrops, which will be a maximum in the case of a 'dip fault'—that is, a fault whose direction coincides with dip. In the case of strike faults a particular outcrop may be either doubled, or concealed altogether, according as the fault hades against or with the dip. These cases can be seen in the following diagram (Fig. 8).

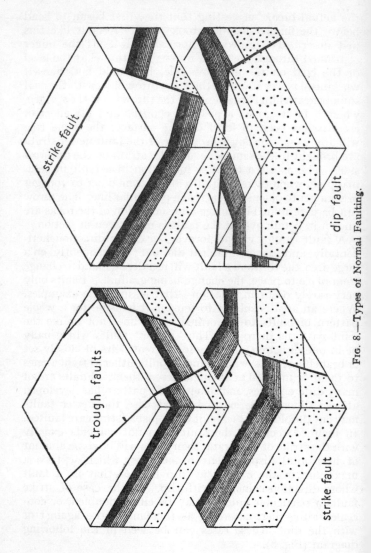

FIG. 8.—Types of Normal Faulting.

It is a general experience to find that where very large dislocations occur there is not one clean-cut fault, but a narrow belt of several smaller faults, throwing down in the same direction, and among them giving a considerable total throw. Such a grouping is referred to as ' step faulting '. Two normal faults close together and parallel which throw in opposite directions and towards one another form a ' trough fault ', the strata between them being in effect let down in a long, narrow trough. The opposite condition, where a rib of strata is left high up with parallel faults throwing down and outwards on each side, is a ' horst '.

When a fault plane cuts shales or similar soft strata the soft, broken material is kneaded together and dragged down the fault plane as a thin layer of clay or ' douk ', sometimes called ' leather bed '. This is very important in all questions of the movement of underground waters, either in water supply or in the problems connected with the drainage of mining areas. In harder rocks the fault produces a zone of smashed-up rock which may act as a fairly open channel for the passage of water. In the case of very hard rocks, or hard shales tightly packed together without much breakage, the planes along which fault movement has taken place may be smoothed and highly polished, and striated in the direction in which the movement has taken place—these polished planes are called ' slickensides '.

In most cases faults make little show at the surface, unless they bring rocks of very different hardness and jointing against one another at the same level. In the case of a fault bringing together very resistant rocks on one side against easily eroded rocks on the other, the soft rocks will erode much more quickly than the resistant ones and a long line of cliff or sharply rising ground may be produced along the fault line. Such ' fault scarps ' are responsible for many of the very striking pieces of scenery in this country. Much of the Pennine edge on the east side of the Vale of Eden, and many of the famous scars—Giggleswick Scar, Attermire Scar, etc.—in the Mid-Pennines, are fault scraps. They must, however, be regarded as exceptional cases. Some faults are marked by lines of springs where the moving water in a pervious stratum is brought against an impervious rock at a fault and is forced out at the surface.

The folding that is found in a complex mountain range is too intricate for discussion in any introduction to geology, but can be illustrated briefly by a few sections. The Highlands of Scotland and of Scandinavia form part of a very ancient mountain chain in which the principal structures are ' fan folding ' and ' thrust planes '. The material forming the mountain chain has been squeezed between two blocks of resistant crust and has squeezed up between them into large folds which have collapsed nearly symmetrically outward, forming in section a large and fairly regular ' fan ' of folds; these are overturned to the outside of the range, and vertical in the middle. At the edges of the range the overturned folds have sheared along the underside limb, and there has been considerable sliding and movement of large pieces of country along these shear planes—the ' major thrusts '. In the more recent mountain chains, such as the Alps, the folding has proceeded to extreme limits, and enormous folds have been produced, overturned and recumbent in the direction in which the thrust took place. The deep dissection that has followed has often separated the front or ' nose ' of some of these overturned folds from their ' roots ', and mountains such as the Matterhorn may, indeed, be carved out of the lower side of such an overturned fold and present us with the unusual experience of a series of rocks lying upside down.

In the large-scale movement of rocks indicated in mountain folding, changes in the physical character of the rocks are induced, the commonest of which is the development of **cleavage**. The constituent minerals and fragments of a rock subjected to great and sustained pressure tend to rotate into such a position that their longest dimension is at right angles to the maximum pressure. As this is accomplished the rock takes on a new ' grain ', and as the mineral that is most commonly produced under great pressure and temperature changes such as take place in mountain building is mica, nearly all such altered rocks have abundant mica flakes ranged along this new grain.

This enables the rock to split more easily along the new direction than in any other, and this splitting is called cleavage. It cuts right across the bedding directions, and is related only to the direction of pressure. Slates are the cleaved, altered muds and shales from such an area of folded rock, and in many slates the bedding, shown by different colour or texture in the different layers, is seen to run across the slabs that split off by the cleavage.

It may be very difficult in some rocks to differentiate in the field between cleavage and bedding, but this distinction must always be made. It is most certainly made by finding a line across which the colour or texture varies and tracing this as a bedding plane across the cleavage. Fine-grained rocks usually acquire a very perfect cleavage; in coarse-grained rocks it is much less well defined, or may be almost absent.

CHAPTER V

Volcanoes. Volcanic products. Igneous intrusions. Bosses, lacolith, dykes, sills. Fumaroles, geysers, etc.

Volcanoes.

AMONG the geological processes seen at the surface of the earth, none is more spectacular or on occasion more terrifying than a volcano in active eruption. Such eruptions have attracted the attention of men from the earliest ages and accounts of eye-witnesses are preserved among many ancient documents. The Biblical story of the overthrow of Sodom and Gomorrah is probably a folk-memory account of the eruption of one of the many volcanoes in that district, which at some not very remote period flooded the neighbouring part of the Dead Sea valley with lavas. The eruptions of Vesuvius and the destruction of Herculaneum and Pompeii have been described by contemporaries, and in the case of Vesuvius we have eye-witness accounts of its various moods and changes for over 2000 years.

In Chapter I it was suggested that there is immediately below the outer crust of continental material a sub-crust layer of more basic silicates which is in a state of very high temperature and pressure, such that any release of pressure will allow the material at once to assume the liquid state. It is material from this layer escaping to the surface that supplies much of the volcanic phenomena, along with a smaller proportion of material from the continental crust itself. There are thus two primary divisions in the origin and nature of volcanoes: those arising from the deeper-seated sub-crust material, of which the lavas are basic in composition, and the shallower types in which the lavas are derived from the acid rocks of the continental masses. All the accompanying phenomena of eruption, lava flow, cone-building, etc., are strikingly different in these two groups, and the differences are also emphasised by the location and distribution of the types.

Deep-seated Volcanoes.

As a result of earth pressures exerted in a radial direction, as distinct from the more usual forces of compression and tension, large slabs of the crust may be fractured into areas bounded by deep faults, the slabs or blocks being tilted slightly. Such a structure forms an area of ' block mountains ', the ranges being formed by the tilted edges of the large sections of crust. Where such a deep fracture takes place, the pressure at the line of tilt is considerably reduced in the sub-crust and the basic sub-crust material may liquify, forming a basic ' magma ' which is extruded up the fracture to the surface. This extruded material makes the lava of volcanic eruptions and, in the case of basic volcanoes, the extrusion points are usually aligned along faults and fractures that are sufficiently extensive to be called ' regional faults '. It is thus common in the basic type of volcanoes to find strings of eruption points, or ' vents ', along the lines of one or more regional faults. In some cases there is a system of several faults such that vents occur in lines crossing a very large area and the volcanic vents occur sprinkled over the whole area. Such is probably the case under the Deccan Plateau, an area of 200,000 square miles, covered by basaltic lavas ranging from 4000 to 6000 feet thick. This great sheet must have been built up by the outflows from countless vents aligned on a great system of intersecting faults occupying most of the area. Such eruptions of magma are referred to as ' fissure eruptions ', in contrast with large single centred eruptions, which are called ' central vent ' type.

The character of the volcanoes of basic type is determined largely by the physical properties of basaltic lava, which is very fluid, having, when freshly extruded, almost the fluidity of water. It is accompanied by very little volatile material and only a small proportion of steam. The eruptions consequently tend to be a rather quiet welling out at the vent, with very little explosive violence, and the lavas poured out will flow for long distances at a great speed before solidifying. This results in most basalt lavas occuring in extended sheets, of very great area, often covering many square miles, but being only a few feet thick. The continued eruptions from a vent or from a series of vents along a fissure thus in time build up a large plateau made up of hundreds of individual ' flows ' or thin sheets piled one on top of the other. Where there is a single central vent, the basic lavas build up a very flat cone of very wide extent, again built of innumerable single thin sheets flowing radially in all directions from the central vent.

The volcanoes of the Hawaiian Islands are perfect examples of the central-vent type. Mauna Loa is the largest volcano on Hawaii, and its cone is built up on the sea floor, its exposed summit forming the main island. At the level of the sea floor its cone is more than 100 miles diameter, and the cone rises to a height of 30,000 feet above the level of the sea floor. At the summit there is a nearly circular ' crater ' approximately 8000 feet diameter, and with bounding, cliff-like walls nearly 800 feet high. The floor of the crater is occupied by lava, the surface of which is ' frozen ' and solid and which is actually the frozen top skin of a pipe of fluid lava rising from the great sub-crust depths. From the edges of the crater the mountain has a slope of less than 6 degrees. On the slopes of Mauna Loa is a second crater, the volcano of Kilauea, at a level of only 4000 feet above sea level, Mauna Loa rising 13,760 feet above sea level.

The crater of Kilauea is a vast oval pit, 2 miles long and a mile wide and in parts as much as 1000 feet deep. The floor of the crater is the top of a lava column, largely frozen over with a solid crust, but with lakes of still-fluid lava here and there. The level of the lava column rises and falls, and the parts that are fluid and the parts near them are in constant activity, with spouts and jets of white-hot lava and small jets of steam. An eruption takes place by increase of this activity, followed by a rapid rise in level of the lava column, until either the crater wall is breached at some weak point or the lava overflows the crater rim. In 1885 the cone of Mauna Loa was pierced at one point by the rising lava column and produced a flow of lava in a stream that extended for 45 miles and which varied from 3 to 10 miles wide and about 100 feet thick. The lava extruded from these craters flows with great rapidity at first, but as the sheet thins out and loses its heat, largely by direct radiation from the surface and partly by contact with the cold ground over which it flows, it becomes more viscous. In this stage it becomes ' ropy ', the sticky lava pulling out into twisted ropes in the final stage before cooling. Along the whole course of the flow the surface freezes over in a thin crust which by the movement of the lava stream is repeatedly broken up and carried forward with the lava. The under-side freezes on to the cold ground and the rapid cooling prevents much crystallisation, so that the underside is generally glassy and slaggy. The upper surface is filled with partly remelted fragments of the broken skin and has a roughly brecciated structure. This difference in structure between underside and top of a lava flow is useful in the field examination of volcanic rocks.

The more common type of basic eruption is that associated with extensive fissures. This type is well seen in the many volcanoes of Iceland. In 1783 there was a large-scale eruption from the fissure called Laki, running for 20 miles in a direction south-west to north-east. Lava poured out of this fissure at many points, forming two principal streams, one at the western part which flowed for 40 miles, and the other flowing for nearly 30 miles. Hundreds of small slag-cones were formed along the line of the fissure a few yards high, all contributing their quota of lava. Hekla, the principal volcano of Iceland, is formed by a fissure which has built up a long ridge of lava-sheets alternat-ing with beds of ' tuff '—that is, the so-called ' ashes ' or volcanic dust and fragmentary material. There is a row of craters along the whole length of the ridge. A great part of the Western Islands of Scotland and the Antrim plateau of Ireland have been built up by basic volcanoes, partly of central type and partly fissure eruptions.

Central Vent Volcanoes.

The prime difference between the acid and basic volcanoes is that the lavas and magma of the acid type are extremely viscous and ' sticky ', and are heavily charged with gases and volatile materials which escape with explosive violence. The explosions accompanying the eruptions produce great quantities of fragmentary material of all kinds, generally classed together under a covering name of ' tuffs '. Because of the viscosity of the acid lavas, the lava flows only a short distance from the vent before it solidifies, and so builds up, with the ejected tuffs, a steep localised cone. Most acid volcanoes thus agree with the popular picture of a steep-sided volcanic mountain, its eruptions being accompanied by emission of smoke, fire and loud explosions.

The magma of the acid volcanoes is derived from the crust of silicate rocks, forming the continental masses, and approximates to the chemical composition of granite or intermedite rocks (see Chapter XVI). The magma may be produced by the liquefaction of rocks along the line of a fault, the tremendous heat generated by the fracturing and friction of the fault zone, and the release of pressure below the fault both contributing. In many cases where mountain folding has taken place the arching-up of the strata has produced an area of relieved pressure in the core of the folds and liquefaction or intrusion of magma takes place there, the liquid magma sometimes ' stoping ' or eating its way upward, by melting the ' roof ' of sedimentary rock against which it rises. Such rising and melting may be very localised and in time produce a thin and weak place in the crust, usually along some already existing line of weakness and, when pressures mount high enough, a break through to the surface is made and a volcanic eruption follows. The acid magmas contain a high percentage of water in their composition, and this exists under pressure as liquid water. When pressure is released, the water evaporates to steam with explosive rapidity, and at the same time other volatile substances in the magma are changed to gaseous form. The gas and steam pressures mount quickly, and as they reach a maximum they break a way through the line of faulted ground to the surface, finding release in violent explosion. Most explosive eruptions start with earth-tremors, which are probably the vibrations set up by explosion and fracture at the seat of the eruption, and these are followed by the forcing out of a vent. The walls of the vent, at first irregular and jagged, are straightened off and the vent enlarged, the torn-off ' country rock ' material being blown out of the vent in ragged lumps of all sizes from the finest dust particles to large rocks of many feet or even yards in diameter. The broken stuff falls around the vent, the coarser fragments near the vent, and the finer stuff further away, often wind-carried for a considerable distance. The preliminary explosions thus build up a first small cone of ' agglomerate ', *i.e.*, country rock fragments mixed with pellets and spray of lava and rock dust. This is followed by the extrusion of lava which is very viscous and flows very slowly. As the lava gets into the lower pressures at the surface, it releases much of its volatile material as gas and the escape of this froths up the surface of the lava into a spongy mass of bubbles and aids and emphasises the stickiness and rapid cooling. Such lavas rarely flow very far beyond the limits of the steeper cone slopes and on cooling they are characteristically full of the steam and gas bubble holes, which are called ' vesicles '. In subsequent periods the bubble holes usually receive an infilling of secondary mineral, calcite, silica in the form of agate, or some other mineral, and the lava is then described as ' vesicular lava '. The explosion frequently blows out vast quantities of molten lava into the air, where the expansion of included gases is so rapid that the whole mass is puffed out into a froth, which on cooling forms ' pumice '.

The rapid cooling and stiffening of such lavas result in the vent or ' neck ' or ' pipe ' of the volcano being soon plugged with a frozen mass of lava stiff enough to bottle up the escaping gases for a time, and to hold them in until they accumulate to sufficient pressure to burst out with another eruption. In this way a volcano may show very intermittent eruption, periods of explosive violence with the extrusion of tuffs and lava streams separated by much longer periods of quiescence, during which the crater has time to weather, to become clothed with vegetation, or even to acquire a crater lake. Vesuvius is the best-known and closest-studied central-type volcano, and its eruptions have gone in cycles throughout historic times. Recurrent periods marked by several eruptions, separated from one another by a few years, are themselves separated by years or even centuries of complete quiescence. Outstanding periods of eruptive activity have occurred between A.D. 63 and 79, A.D. 1036 to 1138, minor eruptions in A.D. 1306, major eruptions in A.D. 1631, and from A.D. 1872 onwards. In each case of renewed activity, the lava plug that seals off previous activity is blown out explosively, and in most cases the explosion is sufficiently violent to destroy part of the old cone. In the case of Vesuvius, Monte Somma is the fragment of an old crater wall, most of the old crater being destroyed in later eruptions.

In some cases the whole of an eruptive episode is marked by a single large explosion. This was the case in the eruption of Krakatoa in August 1883. Krakatoa was a small island lying in the Straits of Sunda between Java and Sumatra and consisted of the emergent top of a high volcanic mountain, mostly under the sea. The island consisted of part of the old crater rim, the neck and plug of the volcano and fragments of lava-flows and tuffs. After a short period of earthquake tremors, an appalling explosion blew away the greater part of the island. The explosion was heard more than 150 miles away and walls and windows were cracked 100 miles away in Batavia. The former site of part of the island was found to be occupied by deep water, the amount of material blown up being about one and one-eighth cubic miles. This was thrown into the air in the form of fine rock dust, accompanied by some quantity of lava spray and ' lapilli '—fine drops of lava—and travelled in the upper air as a dust-cloud for some years. The dust was observed to have travelled three and a quarter times round the earth (a distance of 82,000 miles) before it became imperceptible, and during this period the fine dust in the air was responsible for some of the finest sunset effects that man has ever seen; these ' volcanic ' sunsets had marked effect on many schools of painting and far more than justified the startling atmospheric effects painted by Turner in an earlier period. The explosion set up a violent atmospheric disturbance which passed round the whole earth at a rate of about 700 miles per hour. The sea was thrown into tidal waves rising more than 100 feet above normal tide level. The loss of life by tidal-wave destruction was tremendous, 36,380 people being killed by their effects. Oscillation of the sea level was recorded as far away as Port Elizabeth in South Africa, 4,690 miles, and a great part of the Indian Ocean was strewn with masses of floating pumice.

This explosive type of eruption has occurred in many volcanic areas and in one of its most terrifying forms is accompanied by immense showers of white-hot dust. The cities of Pompeii and Herculaneum were buried under a rain of dust turned to hot mud by the scalding rain condensed from the steam clouds. Such also were the showers or incandescent clouds of dust that overwhelmed the town of St. Pierre in Martinique when Mt. Pelée erupted in 1902. In the course of a few minutes the city with all its inhabitants was smothered in a great depth of incandescent dust which swept down the mountain-side at a tremendous velocity. The lava associated with this eruption was too stiff to flow, and was forced up into the air in a column the shape of the vent, forming a ' spine ' 700 feet high.

Evidence of former periods of volcanic activity are abundant in the rocks of this and many other countries, and in the case of those volcanoes belonging to the earlier geological periods the volcanic centre has often been dissected by erosion to very great depths. By the examination of ancient volcanic centres, a knowledge of the internal structure of the cones, and of the succession of events in their period of activity, decline and final extinction is gained. In this country the volcanic centres of the Lake District, Wales, the Cheviots and many parts of Scotland and

Northern Ireland give us a very complete insight into the normal history of almost all kinds of volcanoes.

In all types of volcanoes the period of extrusion of lavas and explosive release is followed by the eventual extinction of the volcano, with complete freezing up of the vent. At that stage there is still a vast amount of heat in the solidifying magma that underlies the vent area, and this heat has to escape to the surface to enable the final cooling and solidification to take place. An immediately extinct volcanic area thus has many residual heat phenomena which are visible at the surface. Gases of the more volatile substances—sulphur, borax, bismuth, etc.—and steam and carbon dioxide escape through the fissures of the shattered cone and surrounding country, and the places where they escape, often for periods of many years, are called ' fumaroles '. In a few cases these may be of economic importance, condensation sheds are built over the fumarole and in this way sulphur, borax, and some other minerals are obtained. The fumaroles of Tuscany, Italy, are harnessed and provide 30,000 horse power which is transmitted to the cities of Pisa and Florence. The percolation of water through recent volcanic deposits and the water that rises from the cooling magma are charged with many minerals in solution and may be very profitable and valuable ' mineral waters '. Water free from minerals is often discharged at a high temperature, and in Iceland, in parts of New Zealand and in many other recently active volcanic areas, such water is piped to the towns for a perennial domestic hot-water supply.

The most spectacular feature of these areas is the abundance of ' geysers '. These are formed by deep fissures that penetrate the still-hot ground rock and into which ground water percolates. At great depths this water is heated to temperatures far above the normal boiling point, because of the pressure of the overlying column of water. Eventually a temperature is reached where some steam bubbles are formed, which rise rapidly in the shaft of superincumbent water and effect some release of pressure. At this release the bulk of the overheated water in the lower part of the

fissure passes into steam with explosive violence and blows
out all the water in an imposing column forming the
erupting geyser.   This water falls back to the basin of the
geyser, considerably cooled, much of it runs back into the
fissure, and with the addition of ground water the whole
process starts again.   This eruption will occur at fairly
regular intervals over a long period, until either a change
in temperature of the ground or a marked alteration in
the shape of the fissure disturbs the regularity.   Many
geysers can be made to erupt at will by throwing in soap
or some other substance that will cause rapid production
of bubbles and release of pressure in the water column.
The water of geysers is heavily charged with silica in
solution, and this is deposited around the basin in the form
of ' sinter ', a glistening white or coloured crystalline
mass.   In this way the wonderful ' white terraces ' of
New Zealand, and the many wonderful formations of the
Yellowstone Park, U.S.A., have been built up.

In some places the nature of the rock and soil and the
conditions of cooling are such that dying vulcanicity
manifests itself in ' mud volcanoes '.   The heated water
turns the soft and fractured rock material and the unconsolidated tuffs to hot mud, which wells quietly out of the
fissures as lava does out of a true volcano.   These mud
volcanoes are sometimes associated with pitch and bitumen,
derived from organic material enclosed in the tuffs, or
with other important minerals.

Igneous Intrusions.

From the study of dissected volcanoes it is learned that a
period of volcanic activity is usually followed by a period
of igneous intrusion, when remnants of the magma that
supplied the volcano are forced into the upper crust of the
earth, often without sufficient force to reach the surface,
but still powerful enough to fill the fissures and even to
force a way between the bedding planes of the country
rock.   These intruded (in contrast to extruded) rocks
probably contribute to many of the thermal effects just

described as following the extinction of volcanic activity. The Cheviot volcano, of Old Red Sandstone age (see Chapter IX), will afford good examples of many such intrusions. The neck or principal vent of this volcano was made in a country formed largely of folded Silurian rocks, mainly slates and grits. The cone of the volcano was built up of a great many flows of lava, interspersed with agglomerates and tuffs, and must have formed a high cone, resembling, but much larger than, that of Vesuvius. Even to-day, after all the subsequent denudation, the lavas cover an area of more than 230 square miles. The rocks seen in the various sections show the succession to have been, first an explosive outburst which piled up a mass of agglomerate, portions of which remain on the south-west side of Cheviot, near the source of the river Coquet, and are about 200 feet thick. The agglomerate includes boulders of the Silurian rocks which underlie the volcano, and also fragments of older lavas not known anywhere at the surface. The next event was the outpouring of several sheets of rhyolite lavas, seen in the same area as the agglomerates. The main mass of the volcanics is made up of a large number of extensive flows of andesite lavas, mostly purple or dark brown in colour. Many of the individual flows are recognisable by the abundant vesicular cavities in them, and some of the flows have a very slaggy top, evidence of slightly different conditions. Among the lavas are several beds of tuff, representing explosive emissions of dust and 'ashes'.

Near the centre of the Cheviot mass, and covering and occupying the whole of the original vent and some area around it, is now found the Cheviot Granite, nearly twenty square miles in area. The granite was intruded into this position soon after the last of the lava flows and must only have reached a position deep down in the core of the volcano. The coarse crystallisation of the granite and its relation to the other rocks show that it never reached anywhere near the surface and testify to something of the size of the cone. The granite and the surrounding lavas are cut across by 'dykes' of intermediate rock types. The dykes are narrow, wall-like masses of rock, filling nearly vertical fault fissures which run in directions roughly radial from the centre of the volcano, and sometimes extend for miles. The dykes are generally only a few feet thick at most. They represent a final squeezing up of magma material into the fault fractures and fissures that may be connected with the cooling of the granite and the partial doming up of the strata during its injection. This succession is found in most deeply dissected volcanic cones, the order of events being, for a full volcanic and intrusive cycle:—

    1. Explosive outburst with production of agglomerates.

    2. Outflow of lavas with explosive interludes marked by the formation of tuffs.

    3. Cessation of extrusive activity and period of ' solfataric ' activity (*i.e.*, fumaroles, geysers, etc.).

    4. Intrusion of large mass of magma in core of volcanic site accompanied by continued solfataric activity.

    5. Intrusion of dykes and sills in the country rock around the volcanic vent.

It is also found that there is a tendency among the volcanic lavas to show a change in character as the cycle proceeds, lavas which are basic or intermediate in composition in the early stages being replaced in later stages by more acid products. This culminates in the intrusion of an acid plutonic rock in stage 4, but in the dyke and sill intrusions of stage 5 there is generally a reversion to more basic rocks. This change in the chemical nature of the magma is referred to ' magmatic differentiation '—a separation of heavy (basic) minerals by sinking through the lighter part of the melt during the long time that the magma is kept molten, so that material drawn from different layers may have different composition.

Igneous intrusions, as is seen in the case of Cheviot, include at least three types: large central masses, thin vertical sheets—dykes—and ' sills ' which are horizontal sheets (Fig. 9).

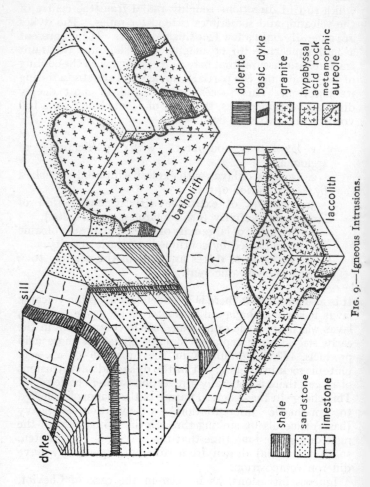

FIG. 9.—Igneous Intrusions.

dolerite

basic dyke

granite

hypabyssal acid rock

metamorphic aureole

shale

sandstone

limestone

batholith

laccolith

sill

dyke

Batholiths.

Batholith is the name given to the large intrusive masses of igneous rock usually occurring at the core of ancient volcanoes and in the core of most large mountain chains. They usually approach the acid type of rock, being generally granite or nearly related to granite in composition. In mountain chains such as the Andes, or the ancient denuded mountain chains of the Grampians in Scotland, there is a succession of large circular or oval patches of granite, arranged along the approximate lines of folding and occupying the core of the upfold. There is no doubt that the magma has moved or been forced into the areas of relieved pressure under the rising fold of the mountain chain. Such masses cut right across all the structures of the country; their outline is generally in fairly smooth curves as though they had melted their way upwards into the strata and melted off all irregularities around them. The sides of the mass dip downward at very steep angles, and no base is found at any depth to which we can reach by ordinary methods. A modification of such intrusion is that known as a laccolith. In these we have a mushroom-shaped mass of igneous rock, forced up a large channel or pipe into regions in the crust where the pressure (weight) of the superincumbent strata could be lifted by the rising magma and arched up. The magma then spreads out into a thick, rounded cake that may be many hundreds of feet thick at the centre, and that slopes away gently on all sides to a thin edge. The base rests on a bedding plane of the rocks and, when deeply dissected, this base can be seen. The laccolites are usually of very acid rock, too sticky to flow easily into a flatter mass.

Dykes.

The commonest dyke-rocks are those of basic composition like basalt and dolerite. A dyke is the filling of a narrow vertical fissure of great lateral extent. Only an extremely fluid magma could flow for the great distances to which a dyke may extend before freezing up. The Cleveland Dyke that cuts across the North of England can be traced from southern Scotland, across the northern counties to the sea-coast near Whitby; it is at least 200 miles long, and from 30 to 80 feet wide.

If the magma filling a dyke fissure reaches the surface, it will flow out into a sheet and become a fissure eruption. Some dykes have done this, and most widespread flows of basalt lavas have dyke 'feeders' to them. Many dykes exist, however, which have never reached the surface and have only been exposed by the denudation of the cover rocks.

Sills.

Magma that is being intruded into the upper crust may, like that of a laccolite, reach an area where it can force its way between the bedding planes of a well-bedded rock and spread out in a wide sheet. When the sheet remains thin and of fairly uniform thickness, it is called a sill. In this country there are several small sills, but the largest is the Great Whin Sill, of Northumberland and Durham. This is a sheet of basic rock, dolerite, which underlies most of County Durham and parts of Northumerland, Cumberland and Westmorland. It is intruded into the Carboniferous Limestone series of rocks. It is a sheet, or rather a series of related sheets of rock, averaging between 80 and 100 feet thick, but at its maximum 240 feet thick; it underlies the south-east part of Northumberland, forming fine cliffs along the coast south of Bamborough Castle. It weathers out into a striking range of inland cliffs across south Northumberland, on the crest of which the Roman Wall is built. It is seen at many places along the Cross Fell Edge east of the Vale of Eden, and its southern portion is seen in Teesdale.

In all these intrusive rocks there is an accompanying feature of great importance: the metamorphism of the rocks into which they are intruded. This, along with the degree of crystallisation, is used to distinguish between volcanic and intrusive rock masses. In the case of a lava sheet and an intruded sill, if both happen to be of similar composition, these two tests will soon determine the true nature of the example being examined. A lava flow is poured out over the surface of the ground, and will bake the rocks on which it lies. This baking or ' metamorphism ' will be very noticeable in shales and softer rocks, and in harder rocks like sandstones may result in partial recrystallisation and change to a quartzite. The upper surface of the lava, however, will cool in air, and will probably be either vesicular or slaggy. The next rocks to cover the lava, whether they are lavas or tuffs or sediments, will be deposited on the cold surface without metamorphism. In the case of a sill the magma is intruded between the rock layers, like meat in a sandwich, and both the under rock and the cover will be baked; there will be no surface exposed to the air, so there will be no escape of gas to form vesicles and no slag. Being shut between rocks which conduct heat very slowly, the cooling will be very slow and there will be time for larger crystals to grow in the cooling sill. On analysis, the rock will also contain more volatile constituents, as these have not escaped in gas bubbles. In the case of a dyke, the metamorphism again will be the same, both sides being equally baked. As dykes and sills often spread for very great distances, there may have been the passage of a vast amount of molten material along a dyke fissure, so that metamorphism of the walls may extend for many feet although the dyke is only several inches or a foot or so thick. There has been a prolonged renewal of the heat with the steady flow of fresh material. These distinctions can be expressed in tabular form as follows:—

	Lava flow.	Dyke and sill.
Crystallisation .	Fine throughout.	Coarser centre.
Metamorphism.	Under side only.	Base and cover rocks or both sides equally.
Upper surface .	Vesicular or slaggy.	Both alike, often glassy on contact surface.
Under surface .	Glassy or slaggy.	
Thickness .	Variable, thinning and thickening.	Constant over long distances.

With the larger intrusions of batholiths and laccoliths, metamorphism may be very extensive, and the crystallisation within the mass is usually very coarse. The metamorphism varies around the intrusion, being most intense in contact with the igneous rock and fading away in parallel zones around the mass. These zones are called the 'metamorphic aureole', and a very clear example can be seen around the Skiddaw Granite of the Lake District and around many of the granites of Devonshire and Cornwall.

When intruded basic rocks crystallise they tend to form a columnar structure and the columns are arranged at right angles to the surfaces of maximum cooling, so that in a sill there is always a tendency to vertical columns, and in a dyke to columns that are at right angles to the walls of the fissure. Dykes cut right across the country, crossing many existing geological structures and cutting through rocks of many different kinds. When attacked by the agents of weathering and erosion, a dyke is usually different in its powers of resistance from the surrounding rock. When it is more freely jointed or softer than the cheek rocks, it will weather out as a deep trench, the hardened, metamorphosed walls even standing up as a prominent lip to the edges of the trench. If, on the other hand, the dyke rock is more resistant than the country rock, it will weather out as an upstanding wall, whence comes its name, dyke being the term used in most parts of the north of England and in Scotland for a stone wall. A sill is usually harder than the sedimentary rocks into which it is intruded and so resists weathering, and because of its vertical columnar jointing generally produces a line of vertical crags along its outcrop. Granite is very homogeneous in texture, with no marked and regular set of joints, so that it weathers very uniformly and produces hills or areas of rounded, even contours, with few outstanding features.

Distribution of Volcanoes.

The distribution of volcanoes over the surface of the earth is one of the most significant features in any study of earth structure and history. While volcanoes are very wide-spread and very numerous, they tend to lie in groupings along main lines or elongated areas. The volcanoes that are still active, or recently active, fall into two main groups. Around the Pacific Islands and the rim of the Pacific Ocean there is a close concentration of volcanoes of central vent type. The western sea-board of the Pacific is strung with 'island festoons' from Japan, through Formosa and the Philippines, by the East Indies and southward to New Zealand. On the northern border are the long string of Aleutian Islands, and on the west the Coast Ranges of North and Central America and the Andes in the South Americas. The whole of this Pacific 'rim' is studded with active volcanoes. Most of the Pacific islands are entirely composed of volcanic rock, the islands being formed by the emergent summit of a series of vast cones, all of the basic type.

From Central America there is a string of volcanoes on the Atlantic islands, through the West Indies, the Azores, Canaries, and the Cape Verde Islands to the Mediterranean, where there are active volcanoes in Italy and Sicily and some of the smaller islands. This belt continues through the Red Sea, by the coastal islands of the Indian Ocean, and by Sumatra, Java and part of the East Indies to link with the western Pacific rim.

In Iceland there is the last phase of activity in a large and geologically fairly recent volcanic field, covering north-west Britain, Iceland and parts of the ridge of shallow water and small islands that fringes the Arctic Ocean. The only remaining major group of active volcanoes is that associated with the 'Rift Valley' of Africa, a line of tremendous trough faulting that runs through a great part of Africa, and a northern branch of which passes through Palestine as the valley of the Dead Sea.

It is seen that the volcanoes of the world are associated with some of the largest structural or 'tectonic' (*i.e.*, folding and faulting) features of the globe, and that the recently active or still active volcanoes are aligned on the newest mountain folds. Extinct volcanoes of previous geological ages are similarly aligned along ancient lines of mountain folding and faulting. In this country there are extensive areas of ancient volcanic rocks in the Lake District, Wales, Scotland, and smaller areas in many widely scattered places. These will be described in a later chapter (see Chapters VIII and XI).

CHAPTER VI

Earthquakes.

THE phenomenon generally referred to as an earthquake is the sum total of the effects of the passage through the substance and over the surface of the earth of the waves of motion set up by any violent release of energy within the crust. The explosions that precede and accompany the break-through of a volcanic vent, or the concussions of a large-scale slip of a considerable mass of sediments, such as frequently happens under the sea on the flanks of the great Tuscarora Deep, off the coast of Japan, all produce earthquake shocks or earth tremors of moderate intensity. The major earthquakes—by far the greatest group numerically, and the most destructive and wide-felt—are produced by the movement of faults and fault fracturing. A fault is produced when tensions or stresses have accumulated in the crust of the earth over a long period, and no release has been obtained either by folding or by flowing of plastic rock ; when a limiting stress is reached, the strata fracture, and a fault is produced with a slip of strata in contrary directions on each side of it. As many regional faults are scores or hundreds of miles long, and penetrate to very great depths through the continental rocks, the friction and jarring along the fault plane with even a very small movement are enormous. It is the energy of this break and jarring that is dissipated in waves of compression and distortion that pass right through the crust and substance of the earth and that are felt and recorded as earthquakes.

Like volcanoes, earthquakes have always attracted man's attention by their terrifying destruction and their apparently uncontrolled and unpredictable occurrence. They are disasters sent by Providence, and entirely beyond the power of man to control. At a very early period the Chinese observers realised that many of the effects of earthquake shocks showed a directional element—tall pillars, buildings, isolated walls, etc., were overthrown more in one direction than in any other and loose objects were often rolled in the same direction. About the third century of our era they built an instrument, the Choko, which recorded the principal direction in which an earthquake shock travelled. This consisted of a mass of masonry, built on very secure and rigid foundation, circular in plan, and hemispherical in shape. At eight equidistant points round it, and some height from the ground, there was arranged a dragon head with mouth wide open and holding a stone ball which is only kept in place by two stumpy teeth at the front of the mouth. On the ground below, and a little in front of each dragon head, sits a toad with wide-open mouth, placed on the same radius of the circle as its corresponding dragon. When an earthquake shock traverses the district the whole structure is vibrated in the line of travel of the shock, and the stone ball is shaken out of the dragon's mouth and thrown in the direction of the shock movement. In the case of the dragon and toad lying on the radius that is in the direction in which the shock is travelling, the ball is shaken out and caught in the open mouth of the toad. In all other cases the shock is not in the same line as the radius on which dragon and toad lie, and the ball falls to one side or the other, and is missed by the toad. After an earthquake, the toad with the ball in its mouth was facing the place from which the shock came, and it was possible to send messengers in that direction to find out where the earthquake had originated. Similar estimates of the direction of the origin of the shock could be made with less precision from an examination of the direction of cracking or overturning of structures.

During the last hundred years instruments have been devised which record accurately not only the passage of earthquake waves, but the nature and degree of movement caused by them. We now know that all earthquakes originate at some depth within the earth's crust, but the

surface effects seem to radiate outwards from a point at
the surface directly over the origin. The actual point or
place of origin of the shock is called the ' focus ', and the
point vertically above this at the surface the ' epicentre ',
of the earthquake. From the focus waves of energy pass
outwards, some being deflected and travelling along the
surface, and others passing right through the mass of the
earth. It is the surface waves which produce the destruction so characteristic of an intense shock.

In 1883 two Italian observers, Rossi and Forel, suggested
that the intensity of an earthquake shock could be recorded
with reference to a scale of intensities. They worked out
such a scale, ranging from the slightest shock with intensity
1 to catastrophic destruction, which they called intensity
10. Their scale was made up of the effects that ordinary
people would naturally notice, so that after an earthquake
it was possible to collect thousands of records and plot
them by their intensity number and the place where they
were observed. The Rossi–Forel scale is as follows:

1. Recorded only by a single instrument.

2. Recorded by instruments of various types, and
felt by a few persons at rest.

3. Felt by most persons at rest and strong enough
for the duration and direction of the shock to be
appreciable.

4. Felt by persons in motion; disturbs doors,
windows, etc.

5. Felt generally; disturbance of furniture; some
bells ring.

6. Awakens sleepers, bells are rung, clocks stopped
and people are disturbed and come out of doors to see
what is the matter.

7. Overthrow of moveable objects, fall of plaster
from walls and ceilings; ringing of church bells; no
serious damage to buildings.

8. Fall of chimneys and cracking of walls.

9. Partial or total destruction of buildings.

10. Great disasters.

When the answers of thousands of people to this series of questions are recorded with the place and intensity marked, the intensities are seen to lie in approximately concentric zones around some centre of highest intensity, which marks the epicentre. By the use of this simple method of observation it was soon made clear that most earthquakes centre round a single spot or are slightly elongated along a line of faulting. Where the epicentre is on a large fault, the intensity zones are usually oval with their long axis along the fault-line. In rare cases there are two distinct epicentres at some distance apart along the fault.

The waves that constitute an earthquake shock are called 'seismic' waves, and the instrument which records them is a 'seismograph'; the lines of intensity are 'coseismal lines'—*i.e.*, lines of equal seismic intensity. The seismograph is simple in principle, though it may be very elaborate in construction. In essence, most seismographs consist of a heavy weight—it may be half a ton or a ton—suspended as a pendulum, either normal, horizontal or inverted. The weight is suspended from a massive framework which is rigidly fixed in a foundation that is taken into solid rock so as to respond as part of the actual crust to any shock. When an earthquake shock traverses the region, the foundation and frame, in common with the surrounding country, are subject to the extremely rapid vibration that constitutes a shock. The actual movement in such case is not usually very much, commonly only a fraction of an inch. The heavy pendulum, by its inertia, is extremely slow to move, and if the duration of the shock is very short, the pendulum will to all intents and purposes remain still in space, while the ground under it moves rapidly back and forth. If the pendulum has a light pen just resting on a sheet of paper fastened to the framework beneath it, the back-and-forward movement of the foundation will be recorded; to record the time relations, the record is made on a strip of paper that is moving at a constant rate beneath the pen and which is marked in seconds or fractions of a second. Modern seismographs make the record photographically, using a fine pencil of light reflected from a mirror on to sensitised paper, and so they eliminate all friction between pen and paper. The records so obtained prove to be wavy curves that can be analysed, and from these we get our knowledge of the nature of earthquake waves and also of the interior of the earth. Referring to Fig. 10, which is an average seismogram, there are three noticeable portions of the curve where the movement, represented by the amplitude or width of swing, is larger than the rest. These indicate that the earthquake shock

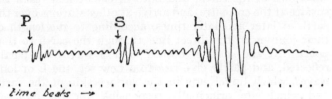

FIG. 10.—Typical Seismogram of a Distant Earthquake.
Showing arrival of P, S and L waves.

at those places was made up of three different tremors, which arrived after one another. We now know that an earthquake shock sets up at the focus two kinds of vibration, or waves, one of compression and one of distortion. The compression wave moves the particles in its path backwards and forwards in the same way as it travels, just as the air moves in a sound-wave. This compression wave, referred to as the P or Primary wave, is the first to arrive at any place, and travels at a high velocity, which is related to the density and rigidity of the material it is travelling through. At and near the surface, in ordinary granitic rocks, the velocity is round about 26,000 feet per second. The next to arrive, and shown next on the seismogram, is the S or Secondary wave, and is one of distortion, the particles being moved from side to side at right angles to its path. This is like the wave that can be sent along a rope when one end is jerked. The S wave travels at about half the velocity of the P wave, and therefore the time that

D—GEOL.

passes between the arrival of the P and the arrival of the S waves, at any place, is a direct measure of the distance from the focus, and if we have three seismograms from recording stations well spread out, we can use this lag between the P and S waves to work out the distance from each to the focus, and so determine approximately the actual site. This is the first approximation that is made within a short time of the recording of a shock, results being telegraphed between several stations and the calculations of distance used. Both P and S waves will travel through the substance of the earth, and both of course first reach the surface at the epicentre, and arrive at other stations over the earth at later and later times, according to the length of their journey in the direct line through the earth to that point. At the surface, both P and S waves are partly reflected, and partly give rise to a new set, the L or long waves, which travel only in the surface skin of the earth and which are principally responsible for the damage. These travel slowly and have also a longer journey between the epicentre and a recording station, as they travel round the curved surface and not along the chord of the arc through the substance of the earth.

The fact that P and S waves travel through the substance of the earth and that we know their properties in great detail has enabled the seismologist (student of earthquakes) to deduce the condition and structure of the interior of the earth from the way in which P and S waves travel through it.

The velocity of propagation of both P and S waves is proportional to the density and elastic properties of the medium through which they travel, consequently if we know the exact distance between the focus (or epicentre) and the recording station, we can calculate exactly what time the waves would take to traverse that distance through rocks of any known density.* When the waves arrive ' before

* For the student with some mathematical interest, it may be useful to give the following formulæ of the rate of travel of these waves.

If the velocity of P waves is V_p, then $V_p = \left\{ \dfrac{\lambda + 2\mu}{\rho} \right\}^{\frac{1}{2}}$

time ', having come more quickly than would be expected, it means that they have travelled through rocks of higher density and greater rigidity than are seen at the surface, and we can adjust these properties to suit the observed times. Differences between the times of travel of the P and S waves and the L waves will check the length of path travelled, and the direction of emergence of the wave when it reaches the surface will indicate whether it has suffered reflection or refraction from a straight line. All the results of this analysis point to a rapid increase of density and rigidity of rocks beneath the crustal layers.

Our most detailed knowledge of the structure of the interior of the earth is derived from curves in which the velocity of the waves, P and S, is plotted against the depth of the chord along which they have travelled. The velocity used is the average velocity, calculated by dividing the time taken for the wave to travel from the epicentre along the straight distance through the earth to the recording station. The time is simply obtained, as by international arrangement all recording seismograph clocks are synchronised, and the difference in time of the record at two places is the time taken for the wave to travel between them. For very short distances where the waves are travelling mainly in the thin skin of continental rocks, the average velocity is about 8 kilometres per second—that is, 26,400 feet per second. As the positions get farther apart and the straight line between them cuts deeper into the earth, the average velocity increases rapidly, until for places nearly one-third of the way round the earth from one another the average velocity is nearly 13 kilometres per second—that is, nearly 43,000 feet per second or 29,000 miles per hour, for the P waves.

This increase of velocity with depth is caused by an

---

if the velocity of S waves is V_s, then $V_s = \left(\dfrac{\mu}{\rho}\right)^{\frac{1}{2}}$

where ρ is the density of the material,
  λ and μ are two elastic constants, the modulus of elasticity in the direction of force and that at right angles to it,
  $\lambda : \mu$ is Poisson's ratio, and k = bulk modulus = $\lambda + \frac{2}{3}\mu$.

increase in rigidity with respect to density of the material of the earth, and agrees with earlier conclusions drawn from the average density of the earth. The increase in velocity is not regular, however, from the crust to the centre and the changes in the rate at which the velocity of transmission of the waves increases are of the greatest importance. The velocity increases steadily with the depth until a critical depth of about 750 miles is reached. Here there is a change, and for some distance below that depth the increase in velocity is only very slow. The way the change takes place can only be explained by accepting here a marked change in composition of the earth and in the physical state of the material. The next great change takes place at 1800 miles depth, where the velocity of the P waves drops back to the surface value and the S waves cease to pass through. On the side of the earth opposite the epicentre there is thus a large circle which receives no S waves. Now, P waves—compression waves—can be transmitted equally well by solids, liquids and gases, but distortional S waves can only pass through a solid; therefore the suggestion at once arises that the inside of the earth below 1800 miles deep is liquid, or in the state corresponding to liquid at the surface. The velocity of passage of the P waves through the centre along a diameter, however, shows that the core must have a rigidity greater than that of the finest steel; hence a great paradox. We cannot state the condition of the earth's core, in terms of conditions which can be observed at the surface. The temperature and pressure must be entirely beyond our knowledge, and the state of matter there is something that to us seems contradictory—matter with the properties of a liquid in response to distortional waves, but with the outstanding property of a solid rigidity.

We can summarise briefly by saying that in this way, and by many refinements of the analysis of earthquake wave records, it is now believed that the interior of the earth consists of a series of 'shells' or zones of material, the inner core of nickel-iron in a state that we cannot comprehend and with a diameter approximately 4300 miles.

Outside this is a layer of mixed metals and silicates just over 1000 miles thick and with a density between 4·75 and 5, the density of the inner core being about 11. A sub-crust layer of silicates, mainly very basic rocks, overlays this; its density is from 3·1 to 4·75, and its thickness about 700 miles; then comes the outer crust of continental rocks, mainly granitic and sedimentary, density 2·75 to 2·9, and its thickness about 40 miles. This upper crust is, of course, of very variable thickness, greatest under the great mountain ranges, thinnest in the oceans, and probably absent from parts of the Pacific basin.

This property of the relation between the velocity of transmission of an earthquake wave and the density and properties of the medium passed through is of the greatest practical importance in modern methods of prospecting. The search for oil or metals can sometimes be carried out over a wide area by means of artificial shocks produced by arranged explosions. This method is described in Chapter XV, p. 295. There are many modifications by which this method of deep probing by means of explosion shock can be applied to the exploration of foundations and to many mining and engineering problems.

Surface Effects of Earthquakes.

Our knowledge of the interior of the earth is based on the records of the transmission of the P and S waves through the earth. The third group of waves generated by a shock is the L or long waves, which travel only in a surface skin radiating from the epicentre. These waves have a rapid undulatory motion, and throw the surface into a complex back-and-forth movement not of very great extent, but of great violence. It is this agitation of the surface that causes the spectacular damage associated with large earthquakes. The rapid shaking of the surface causes any high erection—a tall building, a tower or a large wall that lies across the direction of propagation of the waves—to rock, and if the rocking becomes violent, to break and fall. The amplitude and duration of the L-wave shock are not great, the movement being only an inch or two at most, and the duration rarely more than a few seconds; but the violence is sufficient to wreck very large structures. It has been observed in the earthquakes of San Francisco, and in many in Japan, that buildings that are either light and ' supple ', such as the houses built mainly of bamboo, or steel-framed structures that are resilient to shock, survive much more frequently than those which are rigid and brittle in their structure—well-cemented brick or thin concrete.

The purely surface nature of these destructive waves is shown by the immunity from shock and destruction of certain structures completely isolated by deep trenches. Apart from the destruction to buildings, the effects of long waves are very varied. The soil and skin of weathered rock on mountain slopes are often shaken loose to form landslips, which in many cases have dammed up or diverted river-courses and caused flood havoc. Fissures are frequently formed at the surface of the ground—small cracks in all directions, rather like sun-cracking, and true fissures of great depth and often extending for many miles in a straight line across country. These larger fissures are certainly the surface expression of deep faults, and in some cases they show a displacement at the surface of a few inches or even a few feet vertically, and are often accompanied by a small lateral movement. This is frequently seen in the breaking of railway lines and the shift to one side of the broken ends. In cities this deep fissuring with lateral shift causes great destruction by severing water- and gas-mains and electric cables, the breakage of the gas-pipes usually starting large fires.

In areas of deep alluvium, or in deltas and swamps underlain by peat, there are many curious ' sand-blows '. Circular craters are formed through which great quantities of mixed sand and water are spouted up into the air, which, after falling to the ground, run back into the fissures and craters from which they have come. This is due to the passage of the wave of the shock through water-logged deposits, where the water under compression breaks through the overlying strata, carrying with it a mixture of water, sand and mud. Where beds of peat are present, the peat is torn, and when the sand flows back, an interruption is formed that, in a coal-seam derived from that peat-bed, is represented by a sandstone dyke or intrusive mass. These 'sand intrusions' are well known in all coal-fields, and are one evidence of ancient earthquake shocks.

An earthquake is sometimes accompanied by wide-spread change of level of the land, such as in the New Madrid earthquake of 1811, which affected a large part of the Mississippi valley and formed the Reelfoot Lake, in which a vast area of forest was drowned. Earthquakes in Japan have occasionally altered the land level over a wide area by amounts from a few inches to a few feet. Such changes, acting along with the shaking of gravels and unconsolidated deposits, frequently affect the flow of springs and streams, in rare cases causing a river to disappear completely.

Secular Movement.

In contrast with the violence of earthquake movement, there is a movement of uplift or depression affecting large areas, even continental in extent, that goes on quietly and unperceived, spread over long geological periods. This upward or downward warping of parts of the crust is called 'secular movement'. In this country there is abundant evidence for such secular movement in the period that has elapsed since the Ice Age and during the time that the land has been occupied by human beings. Around the coasts of Scotland, and many parts of England, Wales and Ireland, there are found 'raised beaches'. Along the coast of South-west Scotland, south of Girvan and towards Ballantrae, the road runs near the sea-shore along a shelf of nearly level land, varying from a few yards to half a mile wide, and about 25 feet above the present high-water level. Behind this shelf is a line of cliffs cut in the solid rock, the cliffs in some places more than 100 feet high. Along the foot of the cliffs is a line of caves, which, when examined, prove to be old sea caves, with floors of coarse pebbles and boulders, and patches of sand, including sea-shells indistinguishable from the existing shore deposits.

A similar shelf is found round much of the Scottish coast, and in many places is backed by the line of ancient cliffs with sea caves and all the signs of active sea erosion. The shelf itself is covered with beach material, and is, in fact, an ancient beach, now raised by secular uplift about 25 feet above the present sea level. Other raised beaches exist at various heights above present sea level, in Scotland at approximately 50 and 100 feet OD. In Scandinavia there are many ' strand lines ' and ancient beaches to be seen in the fiords that intersect the coast, up to much greater heights than the British examples. The date of some of these raised beaches is evidenced by the occupation of the caves both by man and animals of prehistoric periods, evidence that at least they were dry and above sea level in those times. Some ancient raised beaches contain the bones of animals long extinct and dating from before the Ice Age, as at Sewerby, near Flamborough Head, where the raised beach contains remains of elephant, hippopotamus, and rhinoceros.

Evidence of the sinking of land areas relative to the sea is seen in the occurrence of ' submerged forests ' around the coast. At many places along the shore there is found a thick bed of peat with tree-roots in the position of growth, and with prostrate trunks of large forest trees, all now below tide level and extending seaward for some distance. The forest must have grown on dry land, and has been sub-merged by down-warping of the land. The greater part of the southern half of the North Sea is shallow, and its floor is covered with ' moor-log ', a thick deposit of forest peat with tree-trunks and roots. This moor-log is well known to the trawlers, whose nets are frequently fouled in the tree-stumps and often bring up masses of the peat. Among the peat so dredged are stone and bone implements used by early man and the bones of recently extinct animals, all of which prove that the subsidence which drowned this area took place during prehistoric times. Traces of this subsidence are found round most of the British coasts and along many of the continental sea margins, and suggest a very widespread general sinking of level.

The most convincing proof of such widespread secular movements is found in the existence of large areas—thousands of square miles in some cases—of marine deposits of various geological ages, covering vast inland plains. The Russian plains are covered with deep deposits of rocks formed in the seas of Cretaceous and later times; but these deposits, now far above sea level, are still nearly horizontal and unfolded. They must therefore have been lifted gently with the country as a whole. They overlie the worn-down edges of much older and folded rocks. In most of the great plain areas of the world similar evidence exists. These marine deposits laid down over the vast plains that had been carved out of older rocks are again evidence of a previous subsidence comparable to the later uplift. The older rocks had been folded and elevated within the reach of weathering and erosion, that is well above sea level, and then, when reduced almost to a plain (a ' peneplain ' is the geological term for such a condition), the whole area must have sunk to form an ocean basin in which marine deposition could take place.

The fact that there is clear distinction between two kinds of movement—the elevation of elongated mountain chains by severe crumpling and folding of strata and the gentle elevation or depression of wide level areas of the crust—has given rise to much inquiry into the mechanism of crustal movements. In this inquiry the greatest knowledge has come from the study of the force of gravity from place to place, and the variations observed in its intensity. From this study it has been possible in recent years to offer a theory of earth movement and structure that explains the various facts observed, and this theory, with all its many modifications and branches, is generally called the theory of isostacy, a name derived from the Greek words meaning equal-standing or ' balance '.

Isostacy.

Interest in the intensity of the force of gravity was aroused during the survey of part of India. In 1859 an

attempt was made to fix the latitude of two stations in the
Indo-Gangetic plain with the utmost accuracy possible,
these two places then to be the two ends of a base line for
the primary survey. The latitude is determined by the
accurate observation of the position of stars and the
time of their crossing the meridian. The meridian is a
line vertically above the observation place, and is usually
determined by using a plumb-bob. The force of gravity
acts towards the centre of the earth, and a plumb-bob should
thus hang along a radius and be truly vertical to the surface
of the earth. The latitude of the two stations which
lay approximately north and south, the northern one
within less than 100 miles of the Himalayas and the
southern one about 100 miles south of it, was determined
in this way, and the difference in latitude enabled the exact
distance between the places to be calculated. This distance
was also measured by the most careful surveying, and the
two results were found to disagree. The southern station,
Kalianpur, lies out in the Indo-Gangetic plain, and if its
latitude is accepted as measured astronomically, and then
the latitude of the northern station, Kaliana, calculated
from it, there is a serious difference between this and the
observed latitude, amounting to 5·236 seconds of arc.
Pratt suggested, after these results had been checked over
and over again, that the plumb-bob at Kaliana was not
actually vertical, because the great mass of the Himalayan
Mountains rising just to the north were themselves deflecting
the plumb-bob slightly by their pull. The pull of mountain
masses had already been investigated and used in Scotland
in experiments on the mountain Schiehallion in determinations of the force of gravity. Pratt therefore calculated
from the mass of the Himalayas, and their distance from the
point, the pull they would have upon the plumb-bob,
and so got the error they would make in the determination
of latitude. He found, however, that the error should
have been one of 15·885 seconds, or more than three times
the actual error observed. This meant that the mountains
in fact pulled with much less force than was expected,
and many determinations made in mountain areas in other

parts of the world soon proved that there is actually a slight ' deficiency ' in such areas. The pull of gravity is proportional to the distance from the centre of the earth, and so will decrease as one ascends a mountain height, but the extra rock mass of the mountain above the general level of the earth's surface will exert a little extra pull; when the corrections are calculated for these two factors— height and mass—the theoretical pull of gravity for that point is obtained. It was now observed that the measured pull was in all cases less than this calculated pull, over mountains, and that over coastal plains and the ocean basins the opposite was the case. These differences between calculated value and measured value are called ' gravity anomalies ', and it is now clear that in general the anomaly is a deficiency over mountains and an excess over the seas. In other words, it appears as though there is some extra depth of light material under mountains, to compensate for their extra prominence, and of heavy material under sea- basins, which compensates for their lowness.

This can be explained if we think of the crustal masses of the earth as material floating on the sub-crust layers. Where any substances are supported by flotation in some other medium, the mass beneath unit areas remains everywhere alike. If blocks of different woods were pre- pared, of exactly equal cross-sectional area, and floated upright in water, it would be seen that the lightest woods would make the longest columns, and their tops would stand higher up above the water than the blocks of heavier woods, when all were floating in equilibrium. At the same time, so long as all were floating, the weight of each column per square inch of cross section would be the same, the heavy woods making short columns and the light wood long columns. Something of the same idea is applied to the crust of the earth. Mountain masses are regarded as ' floating ' in the sub-crust layer of basic rock magma, with deep roots of light acidic material going deep into that layer. Under the seas there is very little light con- tinental material, and the heavy basic magma comes very near to the sea floor, so that we have either a long column made up of a great depth of light (continental) rock plus a shorter column of heavy (basic) rock, or a column of the same weight made of a longer column of heavy material and little or no light material.

When the different masses of the crust—the continents—are regarded as ' floating ' it is easy to explain secular and other movements. In a major cycle of erosion a newly exposed mountain range must have its ' roots ' sunk deep into the sub-crust layer of heavy magma. As erosion removes the exposed part and reduces the mountain chain to a plain, weight is transferred from the mountains and re-deposited on the edge of the ocean, piling up great depths of sediment. With the relief of weight above the roots of the mountain chain, that area begins to ' float ' higher, and we get gentle uplift. The area loaded with sediment ' floats ' deeper, and we get an area of subsidence or sagging. When this takes place there is considerable release of pressure under the mountain areas, and the basic rocks can become at least plastic, and movement of the sub-crust magma must take place slowly from under the sinking areas to under the rising blocks.

In all areas where sediments are accumulating rapidly this downward sagging takes place, and a ' geo-syncline ' is formed. As this goes down, adjacent land rises and continues to feed erosion processes, and sediments go on accumulating. A limit is reached when the geosyncline sags to great depth and the sediments in it are subjected to high pressures and to greatly increased temperatures at the new level within the crust. When a limiting condition is reached, movement beneath the crust takes place more rapidly and the masses of older rock at each side of the geosyncline move towards one another, crushing and folding up the sediments to form a new mountain chain. With uplift there is again release of pressure, sub-crust material is liquefied and volcanic activity can follow. Probably much of the base of the geosyncline is melted, and this melt, which will be of acid composition, is forced into the core of the rising mountain folds as a granite batholith. Along the edges of the fold there may be both acid and basic volcanic eruptions. With the elevation of new mountains, erosion becomes increasingly active and the whole cycle repeats itself, each new mountain chain tending to be added at the edge of an area of older rocks and folded up against the stumps of the preceding mountain chain.

This relation of mountain chains to the ancient rock masses is clearly seen in all the continents. The great Archæan ' shields ' (see Chapter I) form the central continental masses, with roughly parallel chains of mountains surrounding them, the oldest chains against the Archæan rocks, and the youngest chains on the coastal strip.

SECTION II. HISTORICAL GEOLOGY

CHAPTER VII

Geological time scale. Fossils: Nomenclature, preservation, etc.
Evolution. Geological history of Britain Archæan period.
Meaning of unconformities.

Historical Geology

UNDER this term are included two important branches
of geological knowledge: Palæontology and Stratigraphy.
Each tries to arrange its subject-matter in a more or less
true chronological sequence, Palæontology dealing with the
sequence of life-forms, the evidence of evolution, through
succeeding geological periods, and Stratigraphy arranging
events on the earth in the order of their occurrence from the
formation of the crust to the recent period at which History
begins. The subjects are inseparably related, as the
evidence of fossils is of greatest value to enable the determination of the age of strata which are otherwise un-
dateable, and stratigraphy by its methods can often
arrange strata with their contained fossils in their correct
age order, and so confirm or establish the true succession
of fossil types. For the purposes of both it is essential
to have a standard table of reference, into the subdivisions
of which events can be placed, and which table will have a
time value. The basic principle of stratigraphy is the law
of superposition, that in a succession of strata the oldest
lie at the bottom and later strata are laid on top in the order
of their age. Tables of strata or of geological periods are
therefore *always* written with the oldest at the bottom,
and are read upward from oldest to newest, from bottom
to top.

The rocks of the earth's crust are divided into five major
groups, not of equal time-value; these are distinguished
by names derived from the nature of the fossil content.

The oldest rocks are found everywhere in the world to be a vast series almost entirely devoid of fossils, everywhere underlying rocks with fossils. This oldest group is called the **Azoic**, meaning 'without life'. The next major group is characterised by fossils representing forms of life that are practically all entirely extinct and very different from the forms we know to-day. This division is the **Palæozoic**, meaning 'ancient life', from the Greek words *palaios*, ancient, and *zoikos*, of animals. The next major group contains fossils, many of which have recognisably related descendants still on the earth, and many of extinct forms. This is called the **Mesozoic**, meaning 'intermediate life' group. The newer strata are called **Cainozoic**—the 'new life'—period, as nearly all the fossils in those strata belong to still-existing groups. The older geologists made a simple division into Primary, Secondary and Tertiary, and these names are interchangeable with Palæozoic, Mesozoic and Cainozoic. The newest period, including the Ice Age and present time, is called **Quaternary**, and this and Tertiary are in general use, with Palæozoic and Mesozoic, and the newer form **Archæan**—ancient—instead of Azoic.

These major divisions or **eras** are subdivided into **systems**, or natural groups which are in general easily differentiated by the fossil content and the general character of the rocks. The systems have been named either from the areas in which they were first clearly recognised and studied, or from the character of the strata composing them. Systems are again subdivided into smaller units, but few of these are necessary for our present studies. As the science of Geology was largely developed in England and Wales, the systems are based on the strata of this country and are all well marked. In other parts of the world there is some difficulty occasionally in limiting and defining one system from another, but one set of names and divisions is in general use everywhere.

The following is the complete table of systems, and should be learnt by the geologist as the ordinary child learns the alphabet. The names are used both to describe or

e age of fossils or rocks, or to indicate the period
which certain groups of events took place. The
actual age of rocks in approximate years has been the subject
of much recent research, and the values given in the following table are the ones generally accepted as being reasonable
and probable averages.

ERA.	SYSTEM.	Approximate age of base of system, million years.
QUATERNARY	Recent Pleistocene	— —
CAINOZOIC or TERTIARY	Pliocene Miocene Oligocene Eocene	— 30 — 70
MESOZOIC or SECONDARY	Cretaceous Jurassic Triassic Permian	110 140 180 220
PALÆOZOIC or PRIMARY	Carboniferous Devonian Silurian Ordovician Cambrian	280 310 340 400 500
AZOIC or ARCHÆAN	Pre-Cambrian	1200

The geological time-scale is subdivisible in other ways,
of which the most interesting is to place against the scale
the period when the first fossils belonging to each major
biological group appears, and to mark its extent in time.
In this way we get a striking picture of the order of evolution,
as in the table at the end of Chapter XI.

Palæontology.

Palæontology deals entirely with fossils as the remains
of ancient animals and plants, from the study of which

we may gain a knowledge of their structure and habits, as the biologist does with living creatures. The nomenclature of fossils will at first seem strange and forbidding, as practically all the names used are Latinised forms of either Latin or Greek words and, as they have been invented for each fossil, they have an artificial and unworldly appearance. It is reassuring to remember that the names are made in strict accordance with recognised rules, that they have a very definite meaning and often describe the fossil they name, and that they are international. A work on geology in any language, English, Chinese, Spanish or Russian, would still print the fossil names in the Latin alphabet, and they would be alike and mean the same all over the world.

The two names used are the generic name, which is written first and belongs to a large group, and the specific name, which follows. Each generic name will apply to several species, but there is never more than one species name for any fossil. We may have, for instance, the generic name Spirifer, and many species within the generic group, as Spirifer striatus, Spirifer costatus, and when many of the genus are being described in a list, we might continue Sp. bisulcatus, etc. The species name of a fossil often indicates some characteristic, as in the example Spirifer striatus; the specific name *striatus* is given because the shell is covered with thin striæ or fine ribbings. Some species are named after the person who first described them, or to commemorate the name of some worker—*e.g.*, Ammonites *Bucklandi*, after the geologist Buckland; the termination 'i' indicating a personal name. A termination 'ensis' indicates a place name, as in Cravenoceros *malhamensis*, this fossil having been first found at Malham in Yorkshire. In this book the generic name only will be generally used, corresponding to a surname.

It will be of great advantage to the student to look over, and if permission can be obtained to handle, some of the fossils to be found in most museum collections, taking note of all the specimens in the same genus, spotting the characters they have in common, seeing the 'family likeness'. The differences between species of the same genus will be seen to be less than the differences between genera. Any fossils found during a geological ramble should be compared with labelled specimens in a good collection; a knowledge of perfect and selected complete specimens is a great help towards recognising the broken and fragmentary fossils that form the bulk of ' finds ' in a day's field collecting.

The term ' fossil ' was formerly applied to any object dug from the ground, as the name indicates, being derived from the Latin verb *fodere*, to dig. The earlier works that deal with fossils include under the one head rocks, minerals, archæological objects such as pottery and implements, etc.; but since the rise of geology as a science, the word has by common consent been restricted to animal and vegetable remains which are preserved in the strata of the earth and which belong to any of the geological periods. Thus the remains of an animal from the strata of the Tertiary period or from the Ice Age (Quaternary) would be called a fossil, but those of an animal recently buried would not be so called. Fossilisation implies some change in chemical composition or texture which has led to the preservation of the object. The different modes of preservation are very numerous, and fossils of the same animal may exist in a great variety of forms and substances.

Occasionally a complete plant or animal is preserved, particularly in the more recent deposits, such as in peat bogs or in frozen gravels of the Tundras. In the case of peat, the humic acids which constitute a great part of the peat have a definite preservative effect on animal and plant tissues, though they are somewhat ' mummified '. For such preservation it is essential that an organism should be completely covered by the preserving deposit immediately after death and before any decay can take place. The ancient trees of the submerged forests are an example of this form of fossilisation. In the case of most fossils, little is preserved beyond the hard parts of the skeleton, so that such creatures as jelly-fish and others with no hard skeleton are very rarely found fossil, beyond indistinct impressions. Fossils are most common in rocks of fine grain, such as shales and limestones, where an organism at death is quickly sealed off from the air and from the preying of other animals by a fine cover of ooze or mud. This can fill all vacant spaces, and completely envelops all parts. It may be that during this process there is time for the softer parts to be lost by decay, their place being taken by the mud, but the hard parts—skeleton, bones, etc.—remain. These may or may not undergo further change during subsequent time, but except by metamorphism they are seldom altered beyond recognition, if they have been quickly buried in mud. It follows from the above that the ideal conditions for fossilisation are found most extensively in the sea and only rarely on land, so that most of the fossils we know are those of marine life. Terrestrial organisms that die on land are quickly dissipated by air and weather or by animals seeking food, and their remains do not often find a suitable environment for preservation.

The nature of the preservation of a fossil is closely related to the composition of the hard parts. Animals with a calcareous skeleton such as shell-fish constitute the greater proportion of all fossils. Their shell is of approximately the same composition as calcareous ooze, and the conditions that will produce a limestone from such ooze will preserve in the limestone the original shell. In such cases the internal soft parts are sometimes preserved by ' replacement '. As decay sets in, the soft parts may react chemically with the calcium carbonate of the ooze and particle by particle give place to a minute speck of calcite. In this way a fossil shell broken open may sometimes show a ' cast ', or replacement of an internal organ, in calcite. In other cases the inside of a shell filled with soft ooze as the organism decays forms a mould and the filling becomes a ' cast ', which will generally show very fine detail of the inside of the shells, such as the scars of muscle attachments, gills, etc. In sandy rocks such casts are very common, but often the calcite shell which has moulded the cast has itself disappeared, being dissolved away by percolating water in some subsequent period. Silica, and some minerals such as iron pyrites, frequently react with organisms and effect replacements. When this replacement has taken place very gradually, the cast may preserve extremely fine details of the original fossil.

Some groups of animals have a shell or internal structures made of horny material, ' chitin ', which resists decay and exists long enough to produce very perfect casts. Chitin is frequently replaced by carbon, and so some creatures, such as graptolites, which were originally chitinous, are preserved in carbonaceous matter. The bark of trees is often preserved in coal strata sandstones as a thin carbonaceous layer, retaining all the surface markings of the plant. Another group of fossils that is of value does not perhaps come within the strictest definition of the word; these are the imprints of animal footsteps, the tracks of worms and other crawling and creeping animals, which are preserved in the mud over which they walked or crawled. Such imprints are sometimes filled with a finer mud or sand which makes a cast that separates from the imprint when the rock is broken open and gives a ' fossil ' footprint.

Bones of vertebrate animals are composed of carbonate and phosphate of lime, and replacement may take place, or the spongy tissue of the bones be infilled with some other mineral substance, the whole being preserved. In the case of vertebrates it is uncommon to find a complete skeleton, as the bones soon separate as the tissues decay after death, and they may be washed apart by currents or fall apart by gravity and form isolated fossils. The nature of preservation of a fossil thus varies very greatly with the conditions prevailing at the death of the organism and with the subsequent history of the deposit in which it is found.

Fossils are studied in two ways: either in relation to the strata in which they are found, being then of prime interest only so far as they can throw light on the age and conditions of the strata, or else studied biologically, as the remains of once-living creatures. In the latter case they are grouped as living creatures are grouped, in natural classes of related structure. The first division is the clear two-fold cut between animal and plant fossils, the term Palæobotany usually being applied to the study of the fossil plants, and Palæontology rather loosely applied to that of fossil animals.

Palæontology and stratigraphy are so interdependent that it will be easiest to treat them as one subject, illustrating their principles by a simple and more or less continuous account of the geological history of the British Isles. In this way it will be possible to relate the major geological events that have formed the country as we know it now, placed in their order of occurrence, and against and within them to place the varied procession of life-forms now preserved as fossils, seeing them against the physical background of the conditions under which they lived and evolved.

Geological History of Britain.

Archæan.

Reference to the table of strata on page 112 will show that the group of strata collectively called the Archæan is of immense age, the base of the succeeding Cambrian being probably 600 million years old, and the Archæan period itself as long again. The events of this dawn period of the world's history are very obscure, because both during the immense time of their occurrence and during the vast subsequent time even the most resistant rocks and most stable minerals have had time to undergo alteration of all kinds. It is one of the triumphs of recent research, that in spite of the enormous extent of the metamorphism, workers have been able to recognise with a fair degree of certainty the original nature of the strata now represented only by metamorphic rocks.

In Britain the Archæan rocks form the greater part of the Highlands of Scotland, north of the Highland border-line. This 'line' is well marked now by the sudden rise of the Grampian Hills above the lower ground of the Central Valley of Scotland, the mountain front stretching from Stonehaven on the east coast, running with very little deviation from a straight line, due south-west, through Loch Lomond and the mouth of the Clyde, cutting off the south part of the island of Bute and the northern part of the Isle of Arran. The line continues across northern Ireland, from the Antrim coast south of Fairhead and cutting off counties Londonderry and Donegal, both of which are mainly made of Archæan rocks. In Ireland the ' line ' is not a prominent feature, as in Scotland, though the character of the scenery north and south of it is very different. In north-east Ireland the Antrim basalt plateau covers much of the Archæan area. This line is through most of its length a huge fault, with the folded mountains of Archæan rocks on the north, very resistant to weathering and still forming a massive mountainous area, and on the south, or downthrow side, the softer rocks of the Old Red Sandstone (Devonian) and the Carboniferous, which have weathered out into the undulating country of the Central Valley of Scotland and the Central Plain area of Ireland. The fault, with the two series of rocks brought side by side on the flanks of it, can be seen clearly sectioned in the cliffs just north of Stonehaven on the east, and at several points among the western islands.

The other masses of Archæan rocks are seen in Anglesea and the north shore of the Lleyn Peninsula, and at a few places in the Welsh Borders and Midlands, where small portions of these ancient rocks protrude through the covering of newer strata. The principal areas are in Shropshire, around Church Stretton, where Archæan rocks form the core of the Wrekin and of the Longmynd. A small patch is found on the Lickey Hills near Birmingham, in the Malvern Hills, in Charnwood Forest near Leicester and in St. David's peninsula, South Wales. At Ingleton in Yorkshire there is a small area of Archæan rocks seen below the Carboniferous limestone in the valleys, where their outcrops cause the fine series of waterfalls immediately above Ingleton village. Except in Scotland, Northern Ireland and Anglesea, the outcrops are too small and too scattered to be linked up into a complete picture of the conditions under which they were formed.

The rocks of the Highlands are now a vast and complex system, mainly of metamorphic rocks, schists and gneisses for the most part, complicated by many igneous intrusions, the larger ones belonging to later geological periods, but the greater number of the smaller ones to the Archæan. This series of rocks can be separated into two main groups: an older series of gneisses which form the Outer Hebrides, called the Lewisian Gneiss or the Fundamental Complex, from being the lowest and oldest rock we know, and a series that is younger, the schists and gneisses forming the Central Highlands. Both series are intensely folded and sheared, cut up by faults and traversed by numerous dykes, sills and altered volcanic rocks. No fossils are found in any of these strata, and we have no real knowledge of the condition of the world when they were formed, except that most of the crust was then of primary igneous rock, and sediments were only just beginning to be formed. Above the gneisses and schists, and found only in the North-west Highlands, along a strip of country running from Loch Durness, east of Cape Wrath, nearly due south-south-west to the Sound of Sleat between Skye and the mainland and including the islands of Tiree, Coll and Rhum, and lying between that line and the coast, there is the latest group of the Archæan rocks, the Torridon Sandstone. This is a true sedimentary sandstone, extremely coarse and containing a great variety of pebbles and grains of igneous rocks and minerals, derived from the underlying gneisses and schists. This is certainly the product of the weathering and erosion of the older rocks, after they had been folded and elevated into a range or complex of mountain heights. The sandstones occupy deep valleys excavated in the older series, and down the flanks of the hills in the gneisses and schists there are coarse fragmental beds of the Torridonian (the name given to the whole sandstone group), which are undoubted screes such as form to-day along a mountain slope. The Torridon Sandstone is a deep reddish-brown colour, and its grains are covered with a thin pellicle of iron oxides, such as are found on all desert sandstones. Other characters of the rock proved it to have accumulated mainly under arid conditions.

The fundamental complex group is part of a wide extent

of similar rocks, seen in Scandinavia, Greenland and in North America, and there is now no doubt that the fragments left in the North-west Highlands are the edge of an ancient continental mass, now mostly buried under newer deposits and under the sea. The conditions on this continent must have been spectacular in the extreme. Igneous activity of every kind was prominent on a gigantic scale. There would be no soil for lack of humus, no life, just a vast landscape of bare igneous rocks, standing in naked masses, not softened by soil and glaciation as are the contours to-day. We can make no reliable picture of events, as the time-scale is beyond our imaginative power to grasp —several hundred million years passed in this primeval world, time for mountain ranges and continents to form and disappear, for whole fantastic worlds to form and dissolve. In the last phase of this world we are on surer ground. The north-western continent was formed, and on its surface, among a very mountainous landscape, were large lakes or shallow seas, in which some of the Torridon sandstone was deposited. These lakes gradually dried up, and the area became desert, traversed by great windstorms, the driven sand of which was powerful enough to polish and shape many of the pebbles still to be found in the rocks. The deeper valleys were gradually filled in and buried under the scree material weathered from the surrounding mountains, but how far this process went, we do not know. At a subsequent time the area was slightly folded and submerged, and the first of the fossil-bearing strata deposited across its eroded edges. Somewhere between these two periods of the Archæan the schists and gneisses of the Grampians have to be fitted. They are older than the Torridonian but younger than the Lewisian, but their relations are still obscure. Some of them are probably derived from sedimentary rocks and some from igneous, but we do not know how and when. Here lies one of the fields where the way is still open for abundant devoted research, and where great results may be expected as the science of geology progresses.

From the large areas of Archæan rocks in the ' shield '

areas of North America, Africa and Asia, and the impressive thickness and variety of rocks preserved in them, we know that the formations still preserved and exposed in this country represent only very small fragments of the whole history.

In Anglesea and the rest of Britain the rocks are different from those of the Highlands, and include many varieties. The ' Mona complex ' of Anglesea is mainly related to the Lewisian, as are also those of the Lleyn. There are rocks in the Western Longmynd that are almost certainly Torridonian, and the rest, in Shropshire and Charnwood, include slates and volcanic types that cannot be correlated with any in other parts.

At the end of the Archæan period there was a warping of the crust which produced subsidence of most of the country to the south-east of the exposed Archæan rocks of Anglesea and the Highlands, and the area was invaded by the sea. In this process of submergence marine erosion reduced many of the prominent features of the Archæan landscape, eroding away the hills and filling up valleys. The deposits of the new ocean were then laid down across the worn edges and the old topography of the submerged continent, and afterwards, when once more uplifted into dry land, formed an unconformity. This is a feature that occurs time after time in strata of many ages, and it is necessary to get a clear picture of all that an unconformity may mean. Referring to diagrams Fig. 11, an unconformity is seen in section. An old series of rocks has been deposited in a more or less horizontal position. As a result of pressures and compression, they have been folded into mountainous ridges of anticlines and synclines, and so have been given a dip from the horizontal. The elevated tract thus produced has been subjected to erosion, and a land area produced with a varied topography, hard and soft rocks and structures resisting or yielding to erosion and producing varied scenery. For all this period there is no deposition in the area of the unconformity, the products of erosion being carried away by streams and deposited somewhere else in the ocean basin. After a greater or

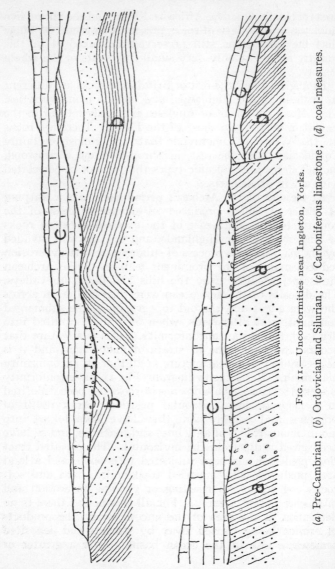

FIG. 11.—Unconformities near Ingleton, Yorks.

(a) Pre-Cambrian; (b) Ordovician and Silurian; (c) Carboniferous limestone; (d) coal-measures.

less time, the land area sinks and is invaded by the sea, probably as some other area of fresher deposits is folded up into a new land area. Erosion produces detritus from the newer land masses, and streams carry the material into the area now under sea and deposit it in strata over the submerged topography of older rocks. The hollows tend to fill in first with the coarser scree and pebble material swept from the submerging land, and, as submergence goes deeper, only finer material reaches the area.

If a second period of compression folding and uplift follows, the old and new strata will be lifted above water once more and erosion will resume its work. Where erosion cuts through the newer cover and exposes the underlying older rocks, an unconformity is exposed. The line separating the older series of rocks from the newer may represent a very long period—all the time taken for subsidence, deposition and re-elevation. Where this break in the succession is large, we speak of a ' major unconformity ', where it is relatively small, we characterise it as a minor one. In the example shown in the diagram, and based on the structure of Ingleborough, the events covered can be tabulated as follows.

1. Deposition of the ' Ingletonian ' series of Archæan age.

2. Period of folding and tilting unrepresented by strata.

3. Gap—period of erosion.

4. Subsidence and deposition of Ordovician and Silurian rocks.

5. Folding and elevation of Ordovician and Silurian.

6. Gap—period of erosion.

7. Subsidence and deposition of the lower Carboniferous strata.

It will be seen that this section of a few hundreds of feet of rocks covers in time the period from Archæan to Carboniferous, not less than several hundreds of millions of years, and that we have at least three continental surfaces present:

the ancient surface of upturned Archæan rocks, that was drowned beneath an Ordovician sea; the landscape of the Silurian continent, with its low, undulating hills that sank beneath the Carboniferous sea; and finally the present European continental surface, of which Ingleborough and its valleys form a part, still emergent above the present oceans. The gaps in the succession are best realised if we remember that in other parts of Britain, where there is no unconformity between Silurian and Carboniferous and where the strata below the Ordovician are present, there is a thickness of many thousands of feet—several miles, in fact —of rocks between Archæan and Carboniferous. In the present example there are also present the records of at least two periods of mountain building. The Archæans were folded into a great mountain chain that crossed Europe and reached into Asia at the one end and parts of America at the other. That folded chain was eroded away and reduced to a normal topography. Later the Ordovician–Silurian strata were folded into another mountain range, that in turn was reduced to a topography much more gentle than the present Pennines, before it was drowned under the invading Carboniferous sea. Periods of volcanicity that piled up the mountains of lava in the Lake District and North Wales passed unmarked in this area. Between the rocks at the base of Ingleborough and those at its summit, evolution had progressed through many major advances. The first formless living specks appeared some time after the Archæan (Ingletonian slates) were formed, and before the Ordovician rocks were deposited life had progressed through most of the invertebrate forms of animals. During the Silurian the first vertebrates had appeared, ancestors of the fish which flourished in the Devonian period here unrepresented, but whose descendants left traces as fossils in the Carboniferous of the upper part of the mountain. Plant life had moved from the oceanic sea-weeds to land forms and had progressed so far as to allow of small forest growth now represented by small coal-seams, as in Meal Bank Quarry, Ingleton, and in the thin coals around the tops of the hills.

When a major unconformity is closely studied, we are bound to stand amazed at the condensation of time intervals now represented only by a line separating two different rock groups. The hand can span a few hundred million years, with the thumb placed on the Archæan and the first finger on the Carboniferous at such an exposure as that seen at Thornton Force, near Ingleton, at places on the Mendips, in Anglesea, and at places in Northern Ireland, where this same major unconformity is seen.

In the account of the geological history of Britain in this and succeeding chapters many major unconformities will be mentioned, and the first impression may be formed that British geology consists mainly of gaps. It must never be forgotten that an unconformity cannot cover the whole earth. Sooner or later, travelling in any direction, we shall come to the edge of the land and pass from the erosional activities of the Continent to the depositional areas of the sea. For every gap in one area there is somewhere else, and not too far away, a corresponding area where the stuff eroded from the ' gap ' is being deposited and is building up new strata. Thus by studying strata over a very wide area it is found that all gaps in one locality can be bridged by deposits in some other, and by piecing these deposits together (that is the peculiar skill and technique of the stratigrapher), a complete and continuous story can be revealed.

CHAPTER VIII

Geological History of Britain: Cambrian; Ordovician; Silurian; Graptolites and Trilobites; The Caledonian ' orogenesis '.

EVERYWHERE in Britain, as indeed over most of the world, the newer rocks rest unconformably upon those of the Archæan system, and are thus separated from them by a great lapse of time. All the newer rock groups contain fossils, and as those found in the Cambrian system—the oldest of the post-Archæan systems—are already in a fairly advanced stage of evolution, it is now certain that the earliest stages in the evolution of living creatures were achieved during some part of the Archæan period, and the remains of these early forms, probably having no hard parts, have not been preserved. It may be that some few fossil remains of them were formed but have been lost in the long period of erosion represented by the major unconformity at the base of the Cambrian. If beds spanning this unconformity are ever discovered, it may be that in them traces of some of the earliest forms of life on this earth will be found preserved.

In considering the physical conditions and environment under which the later rocks were deposited, it is seen that in Britain and parts of Europe the three systems Cambrian, Ordovician and Silurian form a consecutive and continuous group, with no major unconformities between them, and we can therefore treat them as parts of one very long episode —that of the Lower Palæozoic. The Cambrian to Silurian deposits of Britain belong to two main areas. In Northwestern Scotland there is a belt of Cambrian rocks running from Loch Durness to the Sound of Sleat, forming the eastern border to the Archæans; this is a fragment of a northwestern ' province ' about which we shall have more to say. The rest of the Cambro-Silurian lies in a series of masses which surround the Irish Sea. Most of Wales, Counties Wicklow, Wexford and Down in Ireland, the Isle of Man, the Lake District and the whole of the Southern Uplands of Scotland from coast to coast form the second great area.

The general strike of the rocks and the structures in this group is south-west to north-east, and they are seen to be the western end of a belt of similar rocks that runs across the North Sea and into the countries around the Baltic. The eastern parts of this belt in Britain are buried beneath newer rocks.

At the beginning of Cambrian times there was an ancient continental surface eroded out of the Archæan systems, which was being subjected to a certain amount of compression in a direction coming from the south-east towards the north-west. The effect of this was to cause folding, with a ridge of high ground somewhere to the south over Normandy and adjacent parts and a roughly parallel ridge across the Highlands of Scotland. Between them was a depression extending from about the Bristol Channel to the central valley of Scotland, the trough running in the south-west to north-east direction so characteristic of all these systems. This trough continued to sink during Cambrian times and part of the Ordovician, but sediments from the adjacent highland were pouring into it all the time, filling the sinking area at such a rate as to maintain shallow-water conditions for a great part of the Cambrian. For part of the Ordovician period sinking got ahead of sedimentation and the water in the trough deepened, but the downward movement began to ease off, and the story of the Silurian is largely that of the final filling in of the trough by sediments now provided at a rate quicker than the sinking. This movement was of course not uniform or simple; there were occasional contrary movements, several prolonged volcanic episodes, and periods of minor folding of the sediments being deposited; but in the broadest outline the Cambro-Silurian period covers the formation, filling in and obliteration of a large 'geo-syncline'. The period was long enough for vital changes to take place in the forms and abundance of living things, and the fossils found in these deposits illustrate many early ventures in evolution, some successful, many arising within the period, passing through all their stages, and becoming extinct by the end of it, or very soon after.

The Cambrian rocks of Britain are well exposed only in a few places, being almost everywhere covered by great thicknesses of later deposits. The best areas for their study are North-west Soctland, North Wales around Harlech and Carnarvon, a much smaller area in South Wales around St. Davids headland, and two patches on the Irish coast, one at Bray Head south of Dublin Bay, the other farther south around Rosslare and Wexford. There is a small ' inlier ' (that is, a small area lying entirely surrounded as by a frame, by newer rocks) near Church Stretton and the Wrekin.

In the Harlech area the Cambrian is exposed by a large anticlinal fold lying between the synclines of Snowdonia and Central Wales and also by a steep anticline running through Carnarvon. In these areas the lowest beds of the Cambrian are conglomerates and pebble beds resting directly on the folded edges of the Archæan, and formed of the coarse pebbles and detritus swept off the old land surface as it sunk beneath the Cambrian sea. The lower part of the Cambrian consists of many hundreds of feet of coarse, sandy rocks and quartzites which were deposited in the edge of a shallow sea. Towards the middle of the Cambrian finer-grained rocks become more common, indicating that the trough had deepened and the shore-line lay farther away from the area at this time, only the finer sediment being carried out so far before being deposited. This deepening is interrupted for a while during which sandy flagstones were formed (the Lingula Flags of Upper Cambrian), then the deepening is resumed, and the final deposits of the period are about 350 feet of fine silty mudstones which have since been metamorphosed by pressure into the Tremadoc Slates which are so extensively quarried around Tremadoc and between Harlech and Carnarvon. In South Wales there is the same succession of rock types, but the Tremadoc slates have been removed by erosion, and only the lower beds remain.

The massive quartzites of the lower Cambrian are responsible for some rugged though rather bleak scenery between Dolgelly and the mountains behind Harlech. The softer shale beds and the Lingula Flags have weathered out into stream valleys and left the quartzite hills standing out with many impressive crags. The massive rock on which Harlech Castle is built is part of the Harlech Grits. The slate country is generally lower and gentler, as the slates are easily attacked by weathering along their abundant cleavage, and so lie mainly in the valleys.

The Bray Head series is made up of slates, now highly cleaved and represents deposits formed in a deeper part of the trough, probably near the centre.

There is a narrow strip of Cambrian rocks in North-west Scotland, running from Loch Durness to the Sound of Sleat and lying between the pre-Cambrian rocks of the Hebridean group and those of the Grampians. The Cambrian consists of two main divisions, about 150 feet of massive quartzites at the base, followed by a great thickness of dolomitic limestones. The fossils in the lower beds are mainly confined to worm-tracks and traces of sea-weeds, but in the limestones there are trilobites and brachiopods along with a few other invertebrates. The whole fauna is such as would live in shallow water near the shore, but its great interest is that among all the fossils there is none that is also found in Wales and Ireland. All the fauna are, on the other hand, almost identical with that of the eastern part of the United States of America. It seems probable that as most of the animals now fossilised were shallow-water dwellers, they were cut off from the south by deep water near the centre of the trough, but were able to migrate and mingle along a northern shoreline that stretched right across the present Atlantic and across a good part of America. Other evidence confirms this idea of a very extensive geosynclinal trough.

In Wales the Ordovician system follows on conformably, and the lower part of it is similar to the upper beds of the Cambrian, fine-grained shales with a few bands of grit among them. Through the main part of the Ordovician the deposits are progressively finer-grained shales, and the fossils that are preserved in them become of more truly marine character—evidence that the trough was still sink-

E—GEOL.

ing and the sea spreading over a wider area, so that the shoreline was now farther south and north than during the Cambrian. A similar succession is found in South Wales, though here there are among the shales occasional bands of limestone which indicate much clearer water conditions. Probably the trough was widening considerably towards the south and the South Wales area was from time to time out of reach of the fine muds swept from the land areas, and in these clear periods limestone-forming organisms were able to exist abundantly. The maximum period of limestone formation is found in the upper part of the formation, in both South Wales and the Lake District. The final episode of the period is a reversion to more sandy and shallower water deposits, marking the beginning of the last phase of the geosyncline.

The Ordovician everywhere is marked by many pro-longed volcanic episodes, not only in this country, but on the continent and in many parts of the world. It is evident that the crust was unstable, and the minor folding that accompanied the geosynclinal downfolds was accom-panied by deep fracturing, and possibly by melting of some of the sediments in the bottom of the deeply sunk trough. In Wales there are two main periods of volcanic activity to which we owe much of the present scenic charm of the country. Early in Ordovician times there was an outburst of volcanoes at many centres ranged around the Arenig Mountains and Cader Idris, while other large volcanoes became active in Snowdonia a little later. The earliest outburst was in the Cader Idris group, and we must picture a moderately deep, muddy sea, quite out of sight of any land, teeming with life in forms that would be entirely strange and fantastic to us if we could see them living now. Where Cader Idris now is there were rumblings and small outbursts of gases, followed by explosive eruptions that hurled masses of rock fragments and tuff well above the sea. The coarser material fell back to build up a submarine volcanic cone, but the finer dust was drifted by wind and by sea currents for great distances from the cones, so that towards the east and south the volcanic tuffs extend for some distance and gradually thin out among the normal shales. The lavas that were poured out from the volcanoes of Cader Idris and the Arenigs are mainly andesites and rhyolites, and would soon build up cones that would stand above sea level as volcanic islands. There were many different centres from which lavas were poured, and more than one type of lava. These volcanoes continued active through the lower and middle Ordovician, but with the middle Ordovician new volcanoes arose in Snowdonia. Here many thousands of feet of lavas and tuffs were piled up, and, as in the other mountains, they have resisted subsequent weathering far more than the shales in which they occur, leaving the magnificent rock cliffs and ridges that are the keynote of the scenery. The middle Ordovician saw one of the greatest periods of volcanic activity in the whole geological history of this part of the world. The Lake District and Scotland, like Wales, have large volcanic suites present. In Snowdonia the vast rock-faces of Moel Hebog are formed from the earliest volcanic lavas, followed by those of Capel Curig and Snowdon itself. The upper Ordovician was a period of quiescence when the volcanoes became extinct, and quiet sandy deposition in shallower water was resumed. The end of the period, however, is marked by slight folding, and by a large series of igneous intrusions both into the volcanic areas and the surrounding country. The fine rock-faces of Crib Goch and the Moel Trytten are caused by the greater resistance to weathering of intrusive masses, forced at a later period between the lava beds of Snowdon. Part of the great face of Cader Idris overlooking Dolgelly is formed by granitic intrusions among the volcanics. There are many isolated granite masses of this date—Penmaenmawr, and the several rounded hills on the Lleyn Peninsula, Nevin, Llanbedrog and others. Associated with the last cooling phase of these granitic rocks is a certain amount of mineralisation, the most interesting of which is the injection of gold-bearing quartz veins near Dolgelly and much of the copper that has been mined for so many centuries on and around Snowdon.

In the Lake District there is a comparable story, but

differing in detail. The lowest (oldest) rocks are found in Skiddaw and its neighbourhood—the Skiddaw Slates. These are soft greenish slates, too poor and soft to be of commercial use. The basal part of them may even be of Cambrian age. At the time that the volcanoes of Arenig and Cader were getting into their stride, smaller volcanoes became active in the northern fringe of Skiddaw, their lavas building up the Eycott Hills that lie just north of Troutbeck and which fringe Carrock Fell and Blencathra. In the rest of the district there was some amount of folding and erosion taking place, as the Skiddaw Slates are elsewhere followed unconformably by the Borrowdale Volcanic Series. The first member of this group is the agglomerate that forms the foot of Falcon Crag on the east side of Derwentwater, ejected from a volcanic neck somewhere near at hand but now covered by other rocks. A vast series of lavas was poured out to the thickness of many thousands of feet, the earlier ones being submarine but, as in Wales, gradually building a group of volcanic islands formed by the emergent cones. The lavas are interrupted by a few thick bands of tuff—fine-grained volcanic dust—which have since been cleaved to form slates of very high quality—those of Honister, Grasmere and other noted areas. This volcanic phase came to an end, except for very minor outbursts, just as the Snowdon volcanoes were beginning. Again there was a short period of folding, with some intrusion of igneous rocks, and then upper Ordovician time was initiated by a quiet sea in which limestone could accumulate (the Coniston Limestone seen near Coniston and the head of Windermere), followed by more sandy and coarser deposits. The volcanics, again, are responsible for the grander scenery of the Lake District. The Skiddaw slate country has its mountains with grand smooth slopes and a skyline of bold curves, such as are seen everywhere north and west of Derwentwater and Buttermere. At the head and south sides of these lakes the country changes with the Borrowdale Volcanics. The mountains are far more rocky, with steeper and rugged slopes, and a skyline hacked and carved into irregular angular lines, with spikes and peaks in all directions. The rock-faces of Great Gable and Scawfell are carved from the lavas at their thickest, the Langdale Pikes are cut from the southern edge of them. The softer country around Elterwater and south by Windermere and Coniston derives its character from the varied and softer sediments of upper Ordovician and the succeeding Silurian. Eastward the whole of Thirlmere and Ullswater are in the volcanic area.

The Southern Uplands of Scotland, from St. Abbs Head and the Lammermuirs in the east to the coast from Girvan to the Solway, with the greater part of County Down, Armagh and part of Louth in Ireland, are almost entirely built of rocks of Ordovician and Silurian age. The oldest rocks seen are those on the coast between Ballantrae and Girvan, where the series starts with a volcanic centre probably just off the present coastline, from which lavas of peculiar type were ejected. They are basic ' pillow lavas ', so called because, being erupted under some depth of sea, they have been suddenly chilled and solidified in pillow-shaped masses a few feet in diameter, with a very glassy outer portion and the centre part, which cooled more slowly, more crystalline. Between the pillows of lava in all the interstices, there is a mass of chert, organic silica—that is full of radiolaria, minute marine creatures belonging to the lowest phylum of animal life. The whole of the Ordovician is a mass of many thousands of feet of shales, sometimes sufficiently coarse and sandy to form flagstones, but mostly fine-grained black mudstones, with a peculiar muddy-water fauna. The northern part of this Ordovician belt shows a great increase in sandy deposits, and in parts there are thick current-bedded grits that suggest that the shore of the sea is not far away, possibly somewhere near the Highland Border line. This fits in with the picture we have of a broad trough, coarse sandstones near the southern shore in South Wales, sandy and muddy deposits in North Wales, fine mudstones and slates in the Lake District and southern and central part of the Southern Uplands, and grits as we approach the northern shore.

The inliers of Ordovician and Silurian that are seen

beneath the Carboniferous at Crummockdale, Ribblesdale and Malham Tarn, all on the east of Ingleborough, and in Teesdale between High Force and Cauldron Snout, are, by their lithology (that is, their character as rocks and composition), a part of the Lake District group, peeping out from beneath their later cover. Similar rocks have been encountered in deep boreholes near Crook in South Durham. An extension of the Welsh area of lower Palæozoics is found under the eastern part of the Thames Basin and part of East Anglia and Kent, adjoining. They are folded up into a high ridge which stood out as land or was very shallow water during many subsequent periods, so that the later deposits are very thin over the ridge, and it has been encountered in many deep borings. It forms the northern border of the concealed Kent coalfield.

The Silurian is a period that can be summarised as the last phase of the geosyncline; the deposits, like all that form in shallowing water conditions, are extremely variable from place to place, and include, in the lower part, many shales and mudstones, with limestones towards the middle, the clear water being due more to the lack of sediment than to distance from land. The old continental surfaces that provided the many thousands of feet of Cambrian and Ordovician sediments were now worn down to a gentle topography, with slower rivers running down gentler slopes, capable only of carrying finer sediments and muds. In the upper part of the Silurian the fine-grained deposits begin to be coloured and take on some characters that hint at an increasing dryness of climate, and in the Welsh Borders they actually pass upward into marls and flagstones that have many of the characters of mild desert conditions. A similar sequence is found in the Lake District; great thicknesses of shales and thin flagstones with occasional limestones fill up the old trough, and again there is the same sequence in Scotland and Ireland. In most of the areas except the Welsh Borders the upper part of the Silurian is incomplete, and there are, among the beds present, many minor unconformities and traces of folding. The quiet of the earlier Silurian marine landscape was being disturbed by the first tremors and movements of a period of gigantic mountain building. The marine landscape of Cambro-Silurian was preparing for transformation into a continental area of mountains and deserts, and all was in a state of imminent flux and instability. This partly accounts for the innumerable minor variations in the later Silurian strata, seen vertically every few feet, and laterally almost mile by mile.

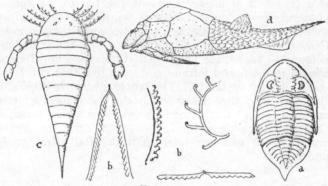

FIG. 12.

(a) Trilobite; (b) graptolites; (c) eurypterid; (d) O.R.S. fish.

The life of the Cambro-Silurian period is both abundant and peculiar. In the first beds of the Cambrian the most noticeable fossils present are brachiopods (bivalve shellfish) and trilobites, with a few sea-weed impressions and worm-casts (Fig. 12).

The trilobites remain the dominant form of life until the upper Cambrian, when, with the Tremadoc Slates, a new form is introduced by the first appearance of graptolites. Brachiopods are essentially a clear-water fauna, and so become more common as the thin limestones of Ordovician and Silurian times are formed. The trilobites and graptolites are extremely useful throughout the period of the geosyncline, because they are groups of animals which are evolving rapidly and are also very widespread, with the result that in the time represented by a few yards of fine-grained sediment, measured vertically, the form of the dominant graptolite and trilobite has been changed. Because of this rapid change, the great masses of sediments can be divided into numerous 'zones' or layers, each characterised by a particular form of trilobite, graptolite or brachiopod, which represents a stage in the evolution of the group that is not repeated. For example, there is a thin bed of flaggy shales at the top of the earliest phase of the Ordovician, that is found to contain a particular form of graptolite, Tetragraptus, an easily recognised, four-armed form, and this thin layer with the same fossil is found in Wales, the Lake District, Scotland and Ireland, always present, and forming a datum line that can be recognised with certainty. The whole system is divided in this way into time-zones which can be recognised from one area to the other and which enable us to say definitely that the Snowdon volcanics are later than the Arenig, and these in turn are later than the Ballantrae group, and so on.

Graptolites.

A graptolite belongs to the phylum Cœlentera, which also includes corals; it is really a colony of minute animals rather like very tiny sea anemones, each individual living in a small cup, numbers of which are strung out in contact with one another along a rod of horny material, each little unit or *polyp* being connected to a common canal or connection that runs through the whole colony. There are no animals now existing at all like them, so that they appear very strange to us and are in fact strange in their apparent evolution from complex early forms to more and more simple forms in later periods. The typical early graptolite, of upper Cambrian, consists of a small float of fine material, rather like a bladder, which floats the colony at the sea surface, and from it there hang down a number of little horny strings, sometimes thirty or more in number, but

later being either sixteen, eight, four, two or one. Along
one side only of these rods is arranged the succession of
polyps in their cups, looking rather like the teeth on a saw,
and being only about that size. Each polyp is a little sac
of living matter, a digestive bag surrounded with a ring of
hairs which can bring the sea-water into the sac by creating
a current, and thus enable the body-sac to extract nutriment
from the microscopic particles of organic matter in the
water. The evolution of the group is marked by progressive
reduction of the number of threads or *stypes*, so that in
lower Ordovician there are four- and eight-styped forms;
these in middle Ordovician become scarce, two-styped
forms being common. In the Silurian there are mostly
one-styped graptolites. At the same time as the reduction
of stypes is taking place there are other changes. The
individual polyp becomes a little larger and plumper
and the stypes first extend themselves laterally in the
four-stype form (Tetragraptus), then in the two-styped
group they either hang like a tuning-fork, extend horizontal,
or turn upwards. When hanging down the polyps are on
the inside of the stypes, so that when they bend outwards
and upwards the polyps are then on the outside, and in the
extreme two-styped form the stypes stand back to back,
and so seem to be a single stype with two rows of polyps.
The one-stype (Monograptus) forms of the Silurian begin
to curve, and by later Silurian times there are some
coiled, watch-spring forms found. Thus, a rock containing
many-styped graptolites is certain to be Cambrian or, at
most, lower Ordovician. Dominant tuning-fork types are
characteristic of middle and later Ordovician, and mono-
graptids (single stypes) are a sure indication of Silurian,
with a further indication that much-curved forms are
likely to be late Silurian. With Silurian, this group of
animals becomes entirely extinct.

Trilobites.

The trilobites are sea-bottom dwellers, belonging to the
vast phylum that includes insects, crustacea, centipedes,

etc. They are again unlike any living creatures, becoming entirely extinct late in the Palæozoic period. The body of the creature has three main parts: head, thorax and tail. The head is covered by a horny shield, roughly semi-circular—the cephalon; the body is segmented with numerous segments that overlap like the joints of a stovepipe elbow, and the tail is again a solid shield which may be prolonged into a spike. Down the whole length of the trilobite there is a raised central portion, with flatter areas symmetrical on each side. Hence the animal has three lobes in either direction, across or lengthwise, and so gets its name Tri-lobe-(ite). Its internal economy is fantastic and must be regarded as an early experiment in evolution that was suited to the conditions of the time, as the group survived a hundred or two million years. The cephalon has a central raised portion in which lies the stomach of the creature, opening directly to a mouth on the under-side. Under the rear part of the cephalon there are traces of four seg-ments, and each, like each segment of the thorax, carries two pairs of legs or arms. The thorax segments vary in number from two to about twenty. There are five seg-ments fused together to form the tail, but they have no legs or 'appendages' under them. The stomach leads to a straight gut that passes through the thorax to an anus at the beginning of the tail. The appendages of each segment consist of two pairs; one of them is a pair of jointed legs hinged near the edge of the central lobe and with a small extension towards the centre. The legs are so hung and hinged that when they move along the sea-floor the inner part scoops up mud and passes it from one to the other in a forward direction, and the ones under the cephalon stuff it through the mouth into the stomach. The second pair, which is placed above the legs on each segment, carries a fringe of gills, by which the creature extracts oxygen from the water as they move through it. Thus we have an animal with its stomach in its head, which feeds and breathes only by walking about on the muddy sea-floor. The jointed thorax allows it to roll up in a tight ball with tail and head overlapping in a solid, horny armour.

In the lowest Cambrian these highly organised animals are already present—evidence of long life evolution in

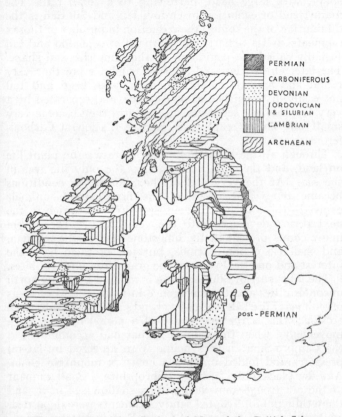

PERMIAN
CARBONIFEROUS
DEVONIAN
{ORDOVICIAN
{& SILURIAN
CAMBRIAN
ARCHAEAN

post - PERMIAN

FIG. 13.—Simplified Geological Map of the British Isles.

Showing the Archæan and Palæozoic formations. All boundaries are simplified, and some small outcrops omitted.

the later Archæan. They are mostly very spiny, and the cephalon is the widest part of the animal, armed with spines that turn back from the rear corners of it. Each segment ends in longish spines, and the tail is usually armed with spines, so that the whole animal is extremely spiny, with large head, narrowing to a small tail. The main trend of evolution in Ordovician and Silurian is the diminution of the spines, the reduction in number of thorax segments, and a remarkable approach of cephalon and tail (usually called the pygidium) to the same size and shape. The later Ordovician and Silurian trilobites are thus very round and smooth in outline, with large head and tail not easily distinguished at first glance, and separated by a very few thoracic segments. Later still they become very small, and finally reach extinction in the lowest Carboniferous strata.

Through all the lower Palæozoic there was no plant life on land, and therefore no animals; the only life was in the sea. At the very end of the Silurian, as conditions became tense and unstable, the first cordate animals evolved—those with a nervous spinal chord, which in the next period developed into the vertebrates. There were many corals present in the limestone seas of the Silurian, and shell-fish of many kinds, but few of them have the interest and practical value of the graptolites and trilobites.

The later part of Silurian time is marked by many small unconformities and the emergence in many places of areas of sediment raised above sea-level and subjected to sub-aerial erosion; this is the first phase of a period of vast earth movements, when the sediments that had accumulated in the Cambro-Silurian geosyncline were squeezed by lateral pressures and folded up into a complex mountain chain. At a few places only, such as in Shropshire, a small remnant of the old trough remained with a shallow sea in it, and there thin and interrupted sandy sediments were deposited, while the rest of the area of Great Britain became mountainous land. The intense earth pressures were produced by the movement of two portions of the crust, one in the south-east and one in the north-west. These moved towards one another, though we cannot speak in any but relative terms and it may be that one remained stationary and the other moved towards it, and between them the trough of thick sediments first sagged and then was squeezed up, as a loose cloth might be squeezed on a table, between two heavy objects sliding over it. The folding produced by this movement was arranged with axes running at right angles to the pressure—that is, from north-east to south-west. The whole of the Cambro–Silurian sediments were affected by this, as well as the pre-Cambrian rocks of Scotland, so that we find all the rocks up to the latest Silurian involved in this north-east to south-west folding. The folds of this period, and the direction they all follow, are both referred to as ' Caledonian ', because they dominate the structure of all Scotland, and the period is spoken of as the Caledonian orogenesis—that is, mountain-forming.

The folds are very complex in the Cambrian to Silurian strata, where there are two or three major folds, anticlines and synclines, very wide from crest to crest, but the flanks of these major folds are intensely folded in the way the tiny ribs of a fan are formed. Imagine a paper fan, with its great number of minor folds, itself allowed to sag into a syncline, then you have a rough picture of Caledonian folding—so-called ' fan-folding '. Caledonian folding is found in the Lake District and in Wales, as well as all other lower Palæozoic areas.

The folding was accompanied by large-scale igneous intrusions, mainly of acid character. The granites of the Grampians, the Cairngorms, Balmoral, many in Aberdeen-shire, some masses in the Lake District, and many smaller intrusions belong to this period. In Wales there are many mineral deposits that were formed in this period—the famous deposits of copper pyrites at Parys Mountain, Anglesea, and many of the lead and copper veins in the Silurian and Ordovician rocks. Some of the copper and lead deposits of the Lake District may belong to the same period. It was this Caledonian folding and the pressure that achieved it that induced the cleavage in some of the finer silts and volcanic tuffs, which produced the famous slates of Wales and the Lake District.

CHAPTER IX

Devonian. Carboniferous. Permian. Hercynian mountain-folding. Igneous rocks and mineralisation.

THE Caledonian orogenesis left the greater part of Northwest Europe as a mountainous continental area, the mountain ranges running as parallel ridges from northeast to south-west, with broad valleys and plains between them, in which remnants of the Silurian sea formed shallow lakes for a time. The climate of Silurian time had been changing towards aridity (dryness and desert conditions), as is clearly evident by the change in the nature of the sediments, from limestones and mudstones to silts and marls of variegated colour. The presence of red and green marls is always evidence that the deposits contain salts of iron in both ferrous and ferric states, giving the green and red colours, and these are always characteristic of dry climatic conditions to-day. There is other evidence of the absence of much rainfall and of desert conditions over the land, with heavy wind-storms. The main deposits of the Devonian period are thick red sandstones, from which the alternative name, Old Red Sandstone, has been given to the formation.

The continental area was over the greater part of Britain, but somewhere about the Bristol Channel position there was a shore-line, south of which lay the sea containing the descendants of many of the living forms that were present in the Silurian seas. In this area marine sediments were deposited throughout Devonian time, and these are now exposed in Devon, from which the name has been given, and Cornwall. It is therefore customary now to refer to these marine deposits as Devonian and to the desert sandstones farther north as Old Red Sandstone, and also to use Devonian for the name of the time interval or period. We will discuss the Devonian rocks first.

The Devonian sea which occupied the greater part of Central and South-east Europe continued the conditions of the Silurian. Fine oceanic silts and muds, interspersed with thick limestones formed in periods of clearer water, are filled with the fossil remains of all kinds of invertebrate life. The limestones are particularly rich in corals and crinoids, which were almost the dominant creatures. Some of the limestones, such as that of Torquay, are quarried, cut and polished for use, and examples of them can be seen in many public buildings throughout the country; the mass of the Torquay limestone is generally of reddish or purplish colour, due to the presence of iron oxides, and the corals stand out nearly white and very prominent against this background. The silts and mudstones between the limestones have been altered by pressure to slate, and are seen to be highly folded by the same pressure, standing with the cleavages and joints at all angles up to vertical, along the Devonshire and Cornish coast. Devon lies so near to the ancient coastline of this sea that there is a striking difference between the rocks of the south and north coasts of the county, the series on the south side of the Bristol Channel including much thicker and coarser sandstones than are found on the south coast. These sandstones and grits form the great headlands of Hangman Point and the coast north of Ilfracombe, while vertical slates make the fine cliffs of Morte Point. There are a few thin limestones in the rocks around Ilfracombe, which contain a fine series of fossils. On the south coast of Devon the rocks are generally finer grained, with more beds of slate and thicker limestones, and are well exposed along all the coast from Torquay westwards. The greater part of Cornwall also is formed of the Devonian rocks, though the cliffs at the Lizard and at Land's End are made by igneous masses of different age.

Britain north of the Bristol Channel and most of Northwest Europe formed part of the mountainous Old Red Sandstone continent. The rising folds of rock left wide valleys between them, elongated in the prevalent northeast to south-west direction, and in these valleys lakes were formed, which persisted through all the period, with occasional interruptions of seasonal drying up. We must picture such a lake covering the Orkneys and Shetlands and the greater part of Caithness, with a range of mountains to the north-west of it and the newly upfolded Grampians to the south-east. Another lake lay south of the Grampians and between them and the hills part of the remnants of which now form the Lake District and Howgill Fells and much of the foundation of the Pennines. This lake occupied all the area of the present Central Valley of Scotland, and an arm of it stretched southwards to include the Cheviot area. North Wales and a great part of the Midlands formed the southern edge of this range of mountains, and they are often referred to as St. George's Land, extending westwards across the site of St. George's Channel and the Irish Sea and forming the hills of which the Wicklow and Wexford Cambro-Silurian area is the remnant. From St. George's Land detritus was carried southwards into the Devonian sea. The lakes are for convenience referred to as Lake Orcadie (from the Orkneys), Lake Caledonia (Central Valley of Scotland), and other more local names for small extensions of them and for smaller areas of occasional water.

The lakes were shallow—so shallow, indeed, that frequently during the period they shrank to very small areas during dry spells, leaving great tracts of mud and silt exposed along their shores. This was fortunate for the geologist, as many plants grew along these margins, and their remains are preserved as fossils. The fishes which abounded in the lakes suffered from the frequent drying up, and among those which survived, some developed internal breathing organs, like lungs, by which they could breath air directly and not only through the intermediary of gills. These 'lung fish' would survive the dry period, buried in the moist mud, but at some stage in their evolution the more virile members left the lake-muds for the land, and from them evolved the primitive air-breathing amphibia, which could live either on land or in water. From the development of an air-breathing lung also we must trace the origin of all our land vertebrates. During the Cambro-Silurian ages we have evidence of sea-weeds in abundance, but it is only in the Old Red Sandstone rocks that we find the first fossils of land plants. It was the coincidence of the development of lungs and the appearance of vegetation on land that enabled the vertebrates to leave the water and find air and food in their new environment.

The deposits that accumulated in the lakes are mainly red sandstones, marls and massive conglomerates, coming down as enormous fans of scree from the mountain slopes, fanning out into the lakes. All the evidence from both fossils and sediments points to a desert climate—long, dry periods, strong wind action and intermittent storms of extreme violence and torrential rains. The rains made temporary flood-torrents which were capable of carrying away rocks and boulders many feet in diameter and piling them far out into the lakes as conglomerates. Some of these are admirably exposed along the coast south of Stonehaven, the most striking of them being seen in the amazing cliffs and headland on which Dunottar Castle is built. The sandstones and conglomerates in that part of the Central Valley are piled up to a total thickness of over 1200 feet, and as they were all deposited in comparatively shallow water, the lake areas must have been sinking as quickly as the detritus was deposited. In Lake Orcadie there are similar conglomerates and sandstones, but they are later in age, an indication that the uplift in that area had been higher at the beginning, or that the lake basin did not sink low enough to become a lake until long after the beginning of the period.

The Old Red Sandstone is divided into two parts, the Lower and the Upper, everywhere separated by an unconformity representing a renewed period of folding. In Lake Caledonia the Lower Old Red Sandstone is interrupted by several major volcanic episodes, the Sidlaw and Ochil Hills, part of the Pentland Hills near Edinburgh, and the Cheviot all being built of volcanic lavas of this age. The lavas are mainly andesites, with not much tuff among them. In Lake Orcadie there are a few volcanic lavas in Caithness, a little later in date than those farther south.

In all districts the Upper Old Red Sandstone tends to be

made up of more and more flaggy beds, and towards the top of the series coloured marls and occasional ' cornstones ' (very impure limestones, which make a good top dressing for corn-growing land) are increasingly common. All the deposits indicate that the severe desert conditions of Lower Old Red Sandstone were progressively modified in Upper Old Red Sandstone time, the lakes becoming deeper and more permanent, the mountains worn down to gentler slopes, so that the streams were less violent and finer material was being carried into the basins.

In the south-west of England and parts of South Wales there is a large area of Old Red Sandstone deposited along the south face of St. George's land, mainly thick red sandstones, a few conglomerates, and in the upper part marls and silts. These grade southwards into the marine Devonian, though the sequence is obscured by the wide area of the Bristol Channel.

The life of the period is most interesting, as it is a period of vital changes in the habits of many groups. The fishes which probably originated in the late Silurian first become common as fossils and belong to groups now extinct. The fishes were covered with bony armour or large scales, and some had their heads completely encased in a bony protection, sometimes covered with hard enamel. The fishes present in the two northern lakes were of different genera, indicating that there was no connection between the lakes in any part. The Trilobites had disappeared, but their place was taken by closely related creatures rather like giant scorpions—the Eurypterids. These creatures were segmented like the trilobites, with long, pointed tails and large limbs on the head segments, with claws rather like the fore-limbs of a lobster, but without limbs on the body segments. The Eurypterids grew to giant size, some of them being 6 feet long. Some of the finest specimens can be seen in the museums at South Kensington, in the geological section. Fragments of tree-trunks and of many plants are drifted in among the silts of the lakes, and among them are a few remains of shrimps and some myriapods (centipedes), and it is probable that in the sparse woodlands of the land, insects had evolved, which were the ancestors of the great variety of insects that flourished in the forests of the Coal Measures.

The movement of subsidence that produced the deepening of the Old Red Sandstone lakes was the first intimation of the beginning of another major geosyncline—that of the Carboniferous. In the Central Valley of Scotland and in the Bristol district the marls and silts of Devonian age pass upwards without any break into shaly calcareous beds which are the lowest members of the Carboniferous system, and in these the fossils belong to a continuous series. In the rest of the country the Old Red Sandstone surface was still very hilly, though the higher mountains had been reduced by erosion, and this topography was gradually submerged beneath the sea which spread northwards as the land sank. Naturally, for a long time the higher parts of the mountain ranges stood up as long islands with deep troughs of sea between them, so that the Lower Carboniferous deposits belong to many different basins, separated by ridges of dry land. After a time the last of the land had been submerged, but ridges of shallow water still separated the deeper basins, and this persists through all the Carboniferous marine period. As the land sank, the exposed areas from which sediment could be obtained became smaller and smaller, the rivers diminished in volume and velocity, and the water became first muddy, then almost devoid of all sediment, and clear. In the clear water, limestones were formed and piled up to a thickness of many hundreds of feet, and, in the thickest areas, several thousand feet. This group of limestones forms the Lower Carboniferous, or the Carboniferous Limestone sub-system. As in the earlier geosyncline, a point is reached where the accumulation of deposits overtakes the sinking and the sea becomes progressively more shallow. This was accompanied by the appearance of a land area to the north and north-west, elevated by minor folding, and from this land large rivers poured out a flood of sandy sediments which rapidly built up the great deltas of the Millstone Grit, the next subdivision of the Carboniferous. When these were built

up approximately to sea level, large coastal swamps
spread along a belt crossing Europe, through Britain,
North France and Belgium, the Ruhr, Silesia and West-
phalia, and reaching into the Donetz basin of southern
Russia. In these swamps grew the vast forests that
eventually became the coal-seams of the Coal Measures, the
last member of the Carboniferous. The end of the period
is marked by the emergence of a continental area with a
desert climate, with a shrinking remnant of the Carboniferous sea over eastern Britain and a great part of the German
plain, in which the chemical deposits of the Permian system
were formed. That briefly is the outline of the second
great geosyncline, the Carboniferous–Permian or, as it is
more euphoniously phrased, the Permo-Carboniferous.
This led on to the fully desert period of the Trias, which
is interposed between the Carboniferous geosyncline and
the succeeding one of the Mesozoic.

The troughs of the Lower Carboniferous were more
numerous than those of the Old Red Sandstone, and
consequently there is some diversity of sedimentation
at the same time in different parts of the country. The
deepest and most permanent trough was that which
occupied the area around the Bristol Channel, the Forest
of Dean, the Mendips and parts of Wales. Here the Lower
Carboniferous starts with shales which are indistinguishable
from the Upper Devonian, except by the change seen in the
fossils present. These are followed by thick limestones,
which can be subdivided by the corals and brachiopods,
which are the most numerous fossils in them. The limestones accumulated by the slow deposition of the calcareous
skeletons of corals, shellfish and minute organisms of all
kinds; and so a thick limestone will represent a very long
period of time, during which there is an obvious change in
the fossils when examples are examined from the base
and the top of such a series of rocks. Between the bottom
and top of the Bristol limestones a period passed which
would probably be measured in some millions of years—this
was long enough for some of the corals present at the base
to evolve to highly complex forms, and for others to die

out. Hence the limestones can be divided into zones, each characterised by its particular group of dominant fossils. Similar zones are found in all the areas, and can be correlated from one area to another, thus making it possible to compare the events in different parts, in relation to the time-periods marked by different fossil zones.

By this means we can say that in the Central Valley of Scotland and in the Bristol area deposition was continuous from Devonian time into the very first of the Carboniferous, but that in an intermediate trough that lay south of the Cheviot–Southern Uplands ridge and north of the North Wales–Midland ridge, and covering most of the Pennines and north Lancashire and Westmorland, the land was not submerged under the Carboniferous sea until some time later. The earliest Carboniferous rocks in this Pennine province are therefore younger than the basal rocks in the other areas. The greater part of Ireland was submerged under the Carboniferous sea, with the pre-Cambrian areas of Donegal and Connemara and the Cambro-Silurian of the east coast sticking out as islands. In Northumberland the lower Carboniferous is made up of very silty shales and thin, impure limestones, due to the large amount of fine silt eroded from the Silurians of the Southern Uplands. As we come south into Durham and north-west Yorkshire, the lower part of the Carboniferous Limestone is absent, as there was a ridge of land or of very shallow water in that part that was submerged until late in the period. South Yorkshire and the mid-Pennines with part of North Wales were a deeper trough, and contain some thousands of feet of strata of this age in the deepest parts, shaly limestones shales and mudstones in the lower part; but, as the land areas were gradually submerged, and detritus ceased to be brought into the sea, only pure limestones accumulated in the upper part. In Ireland the greater part of the succession is made of thick limestones.

We thus see that the earlier part of the Carboniferous Limestone was deposited in a sea dominated by many island ridges or barriers of shallow water, and the deposits in each basin vary from the others in proportion to the amount of adjacent land from which detritus could be obtained. Somewhere about the middle of the period all the land except the Highlands, the Southern Uplands and parts of mid-Wales and Ireland was submerged, and there was everywhere a clear-water limestone sea. These pure limestones, when elevated into mountain areas by subsequent movement, have given us one of our most interesting types of scenery—the limestone cliffs and pavements, pot-holes and caves of Ingleborough, Derbyshire, the Mendips and many parts of Ireland.

This quiet marine condition was changed by the beginning of earth movements and mountain folding in areas to the north, which elevated land masses from which rivers could bring mud and sand. The limestone-forming organisms became fewer in the muddy waters, and a thick succession of rocks was formed consisting of thick shales interspersed with thin limestone and occasional sandstones. These form the Yoredale Series (named from Wensleydale, the valley of the river Ure of Yore, North-west Yorkshire, where the series is best exposed), and were deposited in sufficient thickness almost to obliterate the troughs and form a widespread but very shallow muddy sea. The thickest development of the shales is seen in Pendle Hill, Lancashire, and around Mam Tor, Derbyshire. With the change to muddy water, most of the corals died out, and their place was taken by two groups of invertebrates that like muddy water—the goniatites (single-valve molluscs with shell coiled in a flat spiral, and chambered) and the pelecypods (bivalve shells like mussels and cockles, which both belong to this group). The mud-banks of this shallow sea occasionally reached the surface, and vegetation grew out over the exposed surface, forming peaty humus, which in later geological periods became coal. In many parts of the Yoredale series there are thin coal-seams good enough to be worked.

There is a curious and puzzling feature of the Yoredale series that is very widespread, not only in Europe, but also in America—the so-called ' rhythmic deposition '. When a great thickness of these beds is examined in detail, it is at once obvious that similar beds are repeated time after time at intervals, and in the same order; there is a ' unit ' of shale, sandstone, limestone, followed by another of shale, sandstone, limestone, and so on. Where the shales and sandstones are thick there may be a thin coal-seam in the sandstone. This unit is repeated scores of times, and must represent a rhythmic element either in the climate or the rate of subsidence or of both. The sandstones may be the product of swollen, rapid rivers, carrying coarse sediment, due to increased rainfall and/or slight elevation of the land which increases their slope. The muds and shales could be carried by slower, gentler rivers, due to less rainfall or to a pause in elevation, and the limestones are due to temporary periods in which there was little or no sediment reaching the sea, either the rivers dried up, or were too slow to carry mud very far from the shoreline. When limestones were forming, corals were abundant, but when conditions changed to muddy water, they would migrate farther seaward to clear water, and their place be taken by the goniatites and muddy water fauna.

About the middle Carboniferous there was an increase in the elevation of the continental area to the north and north-west, with considerable increase in the volume and velocity of the rivers running into the Carboniferous sea. These rivers brought masses of coarse sands and pebbles, which built up large deltas across the top of the earlier deposits. The currents were often strong enough to cut up and carry farther out to sea the upper part of the earlier deposits, so that the new deltas of the Millstone Grit (so called from its use for grindstones and millstones) lie in most parts unconformably upon the eroded Yoredales or Carboniferous Limestone. Like all modern deltas, these deposits are very irregular, thick patches accumulating in one area, distributary rivers breaking through and shifting material in another area. The thickest area lies over the Pennines in Yorkshire and north Derbyshire, where there is often 4000 or 5000 feet of strata, including many coarse sandstones of 200 or 300 feet thick. In Northumberland the Millstone Grit is very thin or absent, and is also thin in the south.

The Millstone Grit deltas finally filled up the Carboniferous seas over all Britain, and left in their place a wide area of brackish-water swamps, traversed by sluggish, muddy rivers, with widespread mud-banks covered by almost tropical forests.

The upper division of the Carboniferous is called the Coal Measures and, over most of the world, this series of rocks includes the bulk of all the workable coal-seams. The vegetation that had spread on to the land areas during the Old Red Sandstone period survived through the Carboniferous, and fragments of drifted plants are found as fossils through most of the sandstones and some of the shales of the Lower Carboniferous. With the growth of the Millstone Grit deltas, shrubs and trees gradually secured a footing on the sand- and mud-banks that accumulated near the shoreline and, when the swamps of the Coal Measures were established, the trees spread very quickly into dense forest. It has been suggested that there must have been considerable change of climate, and this is probably the case, as the forests flourished to an extent rarely seen during all subsequent geological time. The main groups present were coniferous trees and giant club mosses and mare's tails. The little Equisetum, or Mare's Tail, that grows to about a foot high on swampy ground to-day, is the dwarfed descendant of the Equisetales group of trees that grew to 60 feet or more in the Coal Measure swamps. The common fossil Calamites is the impression or infilled stem of these giant mare's tails. The tree Lepidodendron, with its elaborate diamond-patterned markings of the bark, is a giant club moss that again was often 60 or even 100 feet high. Some of the trees bore fruiting cones, like the fir trees of to-day, the cones carrying the male and female spores from which the seed of new trees was obtained. The spores were drifted about by the wind, and accumulated in such vast amounts as to constitute a considerable part of the coal which was formed from the forest remains. A dense undergrowth of fern-like plants gave us a wonderful

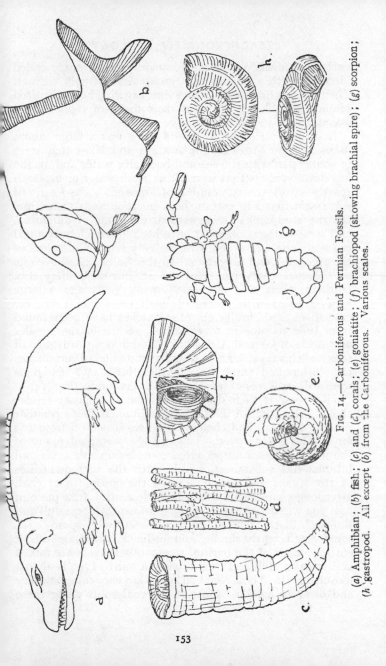

FIG. 14.—Carboniferous and Permian Fossils.

(a) Amphibian; (b) fish; (c) and (d) corals; (e) goniatite; (f) brachiopod (showing brachial spire); (g) scorpion; (h) gastropod. All except (b) from the Carboniferous. Various scales.

variety of fossils, which are commonly but wrongly called 'ferns', as they belong to a group now entirely extinct. Their form is like a fern, with stems carrying finely serrated pinules just like a fern, but their mode of reproduction was different and more primitive.

In these vast swampy forests there was a large fauna, fishes and goniatites in the swamps and lakes that were in connection with the sea and had salty water and, in the lagoons and areas that were either fresh water or brackish (partly salty), a vast number of 'mussels', the fossils of which are found in certain beds by thousands at a time. On the mud-banks there were many kinds of amphibia, and some of the pools must have been like modern tropical crocodile pools, crowded with the very remote ancestors of the crocodiles and alligators. In the shales just above one of the coal-seams (the Hutton) at Jarrow Colliery, Co. Durham, there was discovered many years ago a large area crowded with scores of fossil amphibia, very like crocodiles, and similar crowded patches have been found from time to time in other places. Some of the smaller coal-fields of Central Africa have produced a great range of fossils of this type. There were as yet no higher vertebrates than fishes and amphibia; reptiles, birds and mammals were still creatures of future stages of evolution (Fig. 14).

The trees, at their death, accumulated as peaty refuse, choking the water of the swamps and undergoing a peculiar process of decay and chemical change, sealed-off from the air by the water cover. This change preserved many of the plant tissues, and produced complex organic acids and bitumen-like substances, which, with the vast quantities of tree-spores and pollen, formed the substance of coal, after long compression under later deposits. In a piece of coal you will detect layers of different aspect, some dull and brownish-black, which are almost entirely spore coal, some very brightly shining and jet-black, which are almost entirely made of the bark of trees; other layers are mixed and streaky, dull and bright, while a fourth type is almost like charcoal. These charcoal layers are very thin, powdery and dirty to handle. Most of the coal splits along these charcoal layers into thin blocks. The origin of these layers is not yet fully understood, except that they are made of broken and pulverised wood-cells, which have been completely carbonised.

The upper part of the Coal Measures is in most parts of Britain eroded off, the next strata lying unconformably upon them; but where they are present, as in parts of Staffordshire and Radstock, they indicate a rapid change of conditions. Again, exactly as at the end of Silurian time, red and green marls appear, the vegetation and animal fossils become scarce, and all evidence suggests the approach of desert conditions. This change accompanies the early stages of folding and uplift and rapidly develops into a period of mountain formation, comparable with the Caledonian orogenesis. In this case the principal folds lie in Central Europe, and range approximately east and west, running through the Donetz Basin, South Germany, folding up Silurian and Carboniferous rocks into the mountains of the Ardennes in Belgium, cutting across Brittany, southern England and South Wales, and forming the steep and tightly packed folds of southern Ireland. On the latter part of the train journey from Dublin to Cork, and continuing to the coast at Cork Harbour, the strata can be seen in many railway cuttings to be folded into very steep anticlines and synclines, with Old Red Sandstone in the core of the anticlines and Carboniferous Limestone in the synclines. Similar folding is seen in Gower and adjacent parts of the south-west coast of Wales. In the north the principal fold was in a direction nearly north and south, which, with many complications, gave us the Pennines. In Scotland the Central Valley was dropped by subsidence between great boundary faults that have already been described. The crossing of many smaller north–south folds and the dominant east–west folds of this orogenesis formed a series of shallow basins and domes. In the following period of continental erosion the domes were worn off and the material from them was deposited in the basins, covering the remnants of the Coal Measures and forming our numerous and isolated coal-fields. If it had not been for this cross folding most of the Coal Measures would probably have been completely removed by erosion, and it is therefore a problem of the utmost practical importance to study and unravel the nature and extent of this late Carboniferous folding. By this study it was possible many years ago to predict that there was a deep syncline under a cover of later rocks in Kent, and borings soon proved the existence of a deep ' concealed ' coal-field. The extension of much of the Bristol, North Wales, Cheshire, Lancashire and Yorkshire coal-fields under later deposits has been predicted and studied and now proved, by similar interpretation of this period of folding. The folds of this period are called ' Hercynian ', a name taken from the Continent, where the folds are very well exposed, and we speak of the Hercynian orogenesis, covering the whole period and events connected with it.

It should now be clear that the Carboniferous period has repeated, at least in its main features, the story of the earlier geosyncline of Cambrian to Silurian age, and the desert continental conditions of Devonian time are repeated in the two periods, the Permian and the Triassic, which follow. The end of Palæozoic time is taken at the top of the Permian, largely for palæontological reasons, based on events and remains found on the Continent and only barely represented in this country. The fossils of the Permian are all closely related descendants of the Carboniferous flora and fauna, while some entirely new types are introduced in the Trias. The Permian was a period when most of the British area was occupied by rising land masses, but erosion was going on with sufficient rapidity and effect to prevent any very high mountains being formed in this part of the world. The remnants of the Carboniferous sea were penned up over Central Europe between the rising highland areas, and were cut off as an enclosed inland sea, with its western shoreline abutting against the rising Pennine mass. As the climate was arid, with very little rain and no large rivers, the water of this sea gradually evaporated and the concentration of salts became greater and greater. After a certain concentration was reached, comparable to that of the Sea of Azov (an arm of the Caspian) or of the Dead Sea, lime and magnesia salts were precipitated as a fine dolomite (calcium and magnesium carbonate) mud, which made the Magnesian Limestone that runs from the mouth of the Tyne, south-south-east to Nottingham, as a narrow outcrop. It forms the cliffs of the Durham coast, but at Tees mouth swings inland and forms a narrow belt on the west of the Vale of York and the valley of the Trent. From this come the fine building-stones of York Minster and many other places. As the water became more concentrated, salts of calcium more soluble than dolomite were deposited, and are found now as the beds of gypsum (calcium sulphate) which are mined in the area around Hartlepool and Middlesbrough.

On the west side of the Pennines there were accumulations of desert sandstones and conglomerates washed down by occasional torrents from the Pennines and Lake District hills, now seen as the red, wind-polished Penrith Sandstone and the Brockrams, and as the lower part of similar red sandstone in Lancashire and Cheshire. A small area of Permian strata is also found in Devonshire.

The Carboniferous was on the whole a quiet period, but in the Central Valley of Scotland there were numerous small volcanoes, the necks of which remain as interesting upstanding rock masses, such as the Bass Rock, North Berwick Law, Traprain Law, etc. One of the largest volcanoes is Arthur's Seat, Edinburgh, where the neck with its agglomerates remains, surrounded by lava-flows and traversed by dykes and sills. This is one of the finest exposed and dissected volcanoes that can be seen anywhere, and no student should neglect any opportunity to examine it in detail. There are excellent models and a fine guide-book, to be seen and obtained at the Scottish Museum, Edinburgh. In England there were occasional volcanic episodes in the Coal Measure times, but nothing on a large scale. The majority of the lavas are basaltic in composition, and flowed over wide areas, building up plateaus, many of which affect the scenery of the Central Valley. Around Limerick in Ireland there are a few acid rocks, andesites and trachytes, of this age.   As in the case of other mountain folding and volcanic periods, the last phase is that of large-scale igneous intrusion. This took place during the Permian, and was restricted to the intrusion of the several granite masses of Cornwall and Devon into the axes of the east–west Hercynian folds.   The principal masses are from east to west: Dartmoor, Bodmin Moor, St. Austell, Camborne, Land's End, the Scilly Isles, and Lundy Island off the north Devon coast.   The mineralisation of Cornwall belongs to this intrusive phase, the lodes of ores of tin, copper, lead and tungsten, etc., being formed during the cooling of the intruded granites.

In Devon there are a few volcanic rocks among the Permain strata, earlier in age than the granites, and there are other small areas of Permian volcanics in Ayrshire, East Fife and the Orkneys.

CHAPTER X

The Mesozoic period. Trissaic deserts. Jurassic—the age of giant reptiles. Cretaceous. The age of reptiles. General life of the Mesozoic.

THE whole Mesozoic period constitutes another geosynclinal episode, not so prolonged as the preceding ones, nor marked by such deep downward folding. The whole period also was quiet, and devoid of volcanic eruptions. In the realm of animal life, however, some great strides were made in the progress of evolution, which seems to be proceeding at an increased pace. The period opens with an abundance of new forms of life; the vast army of ammonites, coiled univalve shells related to the goniatites of the Carboniferous, dominated the seas. On land and in the sea also the amphibia were superseded by the reptiles, which rapidly developed to giant proportions, and during the middle of the Mesozoic some of the reptiles took to the air about the same time that a new branch of vertebrates, the true birds, appeared. At the very end of Mesozoic times the first very primitive mammals appeared, and are represented mainly by fossil teeth. The sediments of the Mesozoic are mainly shallow water, very varied, as the seas in which they were deposited were of very varied extent and depth, the floor being itself of an irregular drowned topography, and also subject to repeated minor folding which created shallow ridges and occasional deeper basins. The economic interest is not very great, beyond the iron-ore reserves that are now by far the largest source of iron in Europe, the value of some of the rocks as a source of underground water, and the various building-stones quarried from them.

The Permian landscape which concluded the Palæozoic period was seen to be that of a desert country, with the remnants of an inland sea rapidly drying up and depositing its salts in the inverse order of their solubility. The gypsum beds of the upper Permian are continued in the base of the Trias, but soon give place to beds of rocksalt which are the result of the final drying up of the inland sea in this country.

The much-reduced remnant still spread over central Germany, and its final evaporation there deposited the famous beds of potash salts around Stassfurt and other places.

The disappearance of the sea left Britain an arid desert, at its driest comparable with the Sahara and parts of Arabia. The desert was very hilly: many of the ranges produced by the Hercynian folding and by earlier uplift still stood up above the general level. From these hill-masses torrential streams poured out over the plains in times of sudden storm, but for the main part of the period they were battered only by violent windstorms which swept the whole country with clouds of sand and dust. In the Charnwood Forest, high peaks of granites, volcanic rocks and pre-Cambrian sediments are carved into fantastic shapes, and their surfaces wonderfully polished by this blown sand, which gradually accumulated round them and finally buried them. Over the whole country the surfaces on which the Triassic rocks rest are wind- and sand-polished and reddened by desert weathering, and the Triassic sandstones are 'dune bedded', exactly like the dunes of a modern desert.

The lowest member of the Triassic consists of great thicknesses of slightly cemented sands, streaked in red and yellow colours, reaching its greatest development around Nottingham and over the Midlands. Here it can be seen and examined in a great many quarries, as it makes an ideal moulding sand for the iron founders and is extensively worked for that purpose. In the middle of the Mottled Sandstone, as this formation is called, there is a thick deposit of similar stuff carrying enormous quantities of rounded and water-worn pebbles of a great variety of rock types—the Bunter Pebble Beds. These conglomerates must have been swept by torrents from the high lands still standing above the general Triassic plain, and so far as the rocks forming the pebbles can be recognised, the general movement of them seems to be from south to north; the higher land was generally in the south, with the large range of mountains of Hercynian age sweeping across

France and the extreme south of England, Wales and Ireland. The sands which form the matrix of the conglomerate are not very well cemented, so that while the rock is strong enough to stand in cliffs and excavations, it is very easy to dig with ordinary tools. The Bunter Pebble Beds form the high rock on which the Castle and some of the old town of Nottingham stand, and it is in these beds that the enormous system of underground rooms and passages which underlie much of the old town were cut some centuries ago.

In the Upper Triassic a slight change in climatic conditions is seen in the increasing presence of marls, passing into the so-called Keuper Marl series: fine, wind-blown dust and water-carried silts that were drifted into large and very shallow pools of almost stagnant water. The greater part of Britain and much of Central Europe must by this time have been reduced to a plain interrupted by numerous mountain remnants, as the Keuper marls are very widespread. The lakes often dried up, and the marls contain footprints of animals and water creatures, crystals of salt which formed as the water evaporated, and sun-cracks and rain-pittings which marked the mud as it dried. There are many remains of fish in some of these beds, but, on the whole, the Triassic was a period most unsuitable for the preservation of fossils.

The real end of the Triassic period is marked by a thin, but very important, formation called the Rhætic. This consists of thin beds of marls and shale, followed by very thin limestones—the ' Cotham Marble ' and White Lias limestones—the whole being not much more than 100 feet thick at its very maximum, but being wonderfully persistent over the whole country. It marks the final reduction of most of the Triassic landscape to a plain, at least over all central and eastern England, and the ' transgression ' of the sea across this area, as subsidence began. Small areas of Rhætic are found in Scotland—*i.e.*, in Sutherland, Morven, Mull and Arran—indicating its very wide extent. The outcrop of the Rhætic is traceable across England from Devonshire to the Yorkshire coast. At the time of the

F—GEOL.

first encroachment of the sea over the Triassic landscape there was not much rainfall and little land area still exposed, so that practically no sediment was carried into the new ocean area, and sedimentation proceeded with extreme slowness. The thin Rhætic beds may therefore represent a long period of time. Near the top of this is the famous 'Bone Bed', a pebble bed in which the pebbles are made up of rolled fragments of fish, amphibian and reptilian bones, which have been rolled together by currents just strong enough to remove the fine silts and leave these larger fragments. From this bed we can derive much information about the earliest reptiles and their anatomy.

The Rhætic introduces the Jurassic system, of which the lowest member is the Lias. This formation consists everywhere of finely bedded shales, impure limestones and occasional sandstones. The sediments accumulated in a shallow, open sea, with large rivers carrying abundant sand and clay material from the land areas of the north-west. In the west of England and in Wales many upfolded areas of Carboniferous Limestone stood as islands in the edge of this sea, and at several places—Bridgend, South Wales and many sections near Bristol—the Lias limestones are seen resting directly upon a worn and eroded surface of Carboniferous limestone. The land was still sinking, as the Lias everywhere is found to spread beyond the Rhætic, resting on areas that were islands in the Rhætic sea. The main part of the Lias is a thick series of blue shales and concretionary limestones, typical of a muddy sea area, with an abundant fauna of oysters, gastropods and ammonites. In some of the purer limestone bands there are fossil corals of a type very different from those of the Carboniferous. The essential part of a coral consists of a fleshy body-chamber, roughly cylindrical, with a row of tentacles around the top edge or mouth. The inside of the body-chamber is set with fleshy partitions which stand radially from the walls towards the centre, the whole chamber functioning as stomach and digestive organs. The walls and partitions are supported by plates of calcite secreted by the animal, and the fossil consists of the calcite

	S.-W. England.	Yorks–Lincs.	W. Scotland.	N.-E. Scotland.
Portlandian	Fresh-water passage beds to cretaceous sandstones and limestones.	Marine clays	—	—
	Dark bituminous shale and cementstones	Dark bituminous shale and cementstones		Marine shales, limestones, and estuarine beds.
Oxfordian	Limestones and clays	Limestones	—	Estuarines, limestones, and clays.
	Dark clays	Dark clays	Dark clays	Marine sandstones and clays.
Oolites	Oolitic limestones and clay	Estuarine sandstones, limestones, and shales	Estuarine and fresh-water	Estuarine
	Oolitic limestones, ironstones, and sands	Estuarine	Marine sandstones and marls	Estuarine
Lias and Rhaetic	Blue-grey clays and ironstones		Marine sandstones and shales	Estuarine
	White limestone. BONE BED shales	Shale. BONE BED	Thin calcareous sandstones	—

← deeper water —— deltaic area —— shore line →

Tabular Statement of Jurassic in Britain.

cylindrical outer wall and the pattern of radial and other plates forming the hard skeleton. In the Carboniferous corals the arms and partitions are developed from four primitive ones in the earliest stage of growth, and continue to develop in multiples of four. The Mesozoic corals belong to a type in which there are six arms and primary partitions, and development is by multiples of six. This apparently slight difference in skeleton reflects very vital differences in the anatomy and life-history of the two groups.

In the calcareous rocks of the Lias there are great thicknesses of bedded iron ores, formed under lagoon conditions which have been described in Chapter XIV, page 232.

The sediments of the Lias show very frequent thickening and thinning as they are traced across country, and there is abundant evidence of the uneven subsidence of the area, so that ridges of shallow water are fairly numerous, separating deeper basins. This feature continues through the Jurassic, so that there is considerable difference in local detail between the main areas, such as Yorkshire–Lincolnshire, South-west England, the Midlands and Scotland. There are certain broad features, however, in which the succession in each area is fairly comparable, and these are indications of the wider geographic conditions of the times.

The Jurassic can be divided for convenience into Lower (Rhætic and Lias), Middle (Oolites) and Upper (Oxfordian and Portlandian), and if these divisions are examined wherever they are found in Great Britain, they are seen to give an agreed story. Before giving any detailed account of them, a tabular statement may be useful as guide to the whole series (p. 163).

From this table it is at once clear that in Lower Jurassic times South-west England enjoyed comparatively clear-water marine conditions, with frequent inpourings of fine black muds, but an entire absence of coarse sediment such as would be brought by rivers from adjacent land. The blue clays with ironstones indicate lagoonal conditions, with the area almost cut off from open sea by some local upfolding of the sea-floor. The same conditions spread north-eastwards over Yorkshire and the Midlands, but in the west and north of Scotland the sediments are more sandy, indicating closer proximity to land with rivers strong enough to carry sandy detritus. In the extreme north-east the deposits are described as estuarine. These are sandstones and shales such as would accumulate as sand- and mud-banks in and near the mouth of a river, being partly deltaic, with marine fossils, but sometimes being actually within the influence of the river-water, so that brackishwater or even fresh-water animals could survive. In the estuarine deposits there are often small areas of vegetation which grew on an exposed sandbank, now preserved as a thin coal-seam or a layer of coaly shale.

In the Oolites the south-west is again an area of comparatively clear water, with marine limestones forming during the greater part of the time. These are all oolitic— that means they are made up of minute spherical concretions of limestones, the ooliths, which may have been formed in the bottom of a limy lagoon around particles of sand or fragments of shell which were being rolled about by gentle currents. The fossils of the oolites include many corals which demand fairly clear water. In the Midlands and Yorkshire the oolitic limestones are mixed in among estuarine sandstones which were the product of a large and very variable river delta. In some parts of the estuarines there are thin coal-seams and there are frequent beds of plant remains from which a considerable knowledge of the flora of the time has been obtained. This gives us a picture of a continental area not very far away, clothed with forests having a great variety of trees and an abundant undergrowth of shrubs and ferns, but as yet no flowering plants are known. At some horizons among the sandstones there are large areas of ripple markings—the fossil shoresand of these ancient seas—and across these ripple-marked sands wandering reptiles have left their footprints. Many of these can be seen in the fallen slabs of sandstone along the foot of the cliffs near Claughton, just north of Scarborough.

The Oolite conditions were ended by a general subsidence producing a deeper sea, in which dark grey clays were deposited to a great thickness. These are very well known in the Oxford district, from which they have been called the Oxford Clay, and, with some other associated sediments, they form the Oxfordian. The fossils in these clays are all marine, ammonites and other shellfish, and marine reptiles and fishes. The upper part passes into limestones and calcareous (limy) shales, which suggests that such land as had been contributing sediment was now much smaller, or the rivers flowing from it were bringing less material. The marine conditions spread over the whole country, even into the north of Scotland; but there were still occasional estuarine sandstones mixed in with the finer clays and limestones. It seems, then, as though the Oxfordian represents a very widespread marine episode, with far less upstanding land than in any of the previous periods of the Jurassic, and it seems to indicate an approach towards the middle of the geosynclinal history.

The last phase of the Jurassic shows wide divergence between the south and north. In the south and south-west there was a rapid shallowing of the water, and in some areas around the south coast—Portland and Purbeck—the marine conditions were replaced by a vast fresh-water lake, with a land barrier between it and the still-marine area of Yorkshire and Lincolnshire. This upper series is not present in Scotland, although it may have been deposited, then eroded away in later times. Around the shores of this fresh-water lake there were forests of peculiar trees—the Cycads—to which group belong the pineapples. Along with abundant tree remains there are many insects preserved and traces of the first ancestral mammals.

The Jurassic is followed by the great series of Chalk beds, belonging to the Cretaceous system; but the base of the Cretaceous is formed of 'passage beds' intermediate in character and the result of changing conditions which introduced the chalk sea. It is certain, from the study of the strata of Russia and other parts of the Continent, that towards the end of Jurassic times there was an open sea to the north-east, in the western edge of which the upper clays of the Yorkshire coast were deposited, as the same fossils are present in similar clays stretching right across Europe into Russia. This northern sea was cut off across the Midlands by a ridge of older (Palæozoic) rocks which had been folded up by minor earth movements, and to the south of the ridge was the fresh-water lake just mentioned, which stretched across parts of Belgium and France. The Cretaceous was introduced by very widespread subsidence, which was jerky and irregular in its incidence, so that there were many alternations between sandy and muddy conditions. During this subsidence more than 2500 feet of shallow-water sediments were deposited over South-east England, keeping pace with the subsidence, so that the top of the sediments was always near water level. These sediments were derived in the main from Jurassic strata freshly exposed by the folding, so that they are identical in composition with them. The subsidence soon connected the fresh-water lake with the sea, and the sediments and fossils become marine in character.

In the more northerly parts the subsidence produced many thick clays rich in muddy-water marine animals, passing upwards into a bed of red chalk, a fine chalk or lime mud stained with iron oxides, which in turn is followed by the true white chalk. The chalk is everywhere surprisingly uniform in character and very widespread, being found across the whole of the British Isles and across the continental areas of much of the world. The chalk sea is said to be ' transgressive '—that is, it gradually spread across the land surfaces, spreading wider and wider until very little land was left exposed over a great part of the present land areas. Such a world-wide transgression as this could only have been accomplished by the upfolding of some of the deeper ocean floor, so that the volume of the sea spread out over a greatly extended but shallower area. This upfolding and spilling of the sea across the land was the precursor of the next big period of mountain-building which ended this geosynclinal episode. The chalk everywhere consists of the finest chalk mud, mainly composed of minute animals with a lime skeleton, fragments of shells, and a fine chalky matrix that is almost too fine to determine under the microscope. There is remarkably little sediment in the chalk, due to the drowning of such a large area of land and suspension of erosion over the drowned areas.

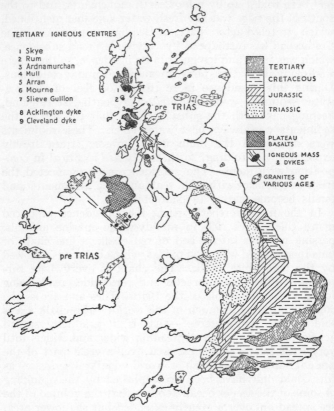

FIG. 15.—Simplified Geological Map of the British Isles.

Showing the Mesozoic and Tertiary formations, and the Tertiary Igneous Centres. Some small outcrops omitted.

As the Jurassic and Cretaceous rocks form the greater part of all the country south and east of a line from the North Yorkshire coast to Bristol, then south to the south coast (see map, Fig. 15), they will provide much of the field-work for the greater part of the population of Britain. Because of their nearness to the older universities, to London, and to the big centres of population of the south-east, and because they are nearly everywhere richly fossiliferous

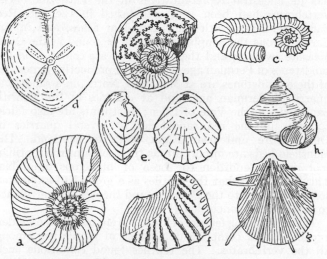

FIG. 16.—Mesozoic Fossils.

(*a, b, c*) Ammonites—(*b*) shows sutures, (*c*) uncoiling; (*d*) echino-derm (sea urchin); (*e*) brachiopod; (*f, g*) pelecypods; (*h*) gastropod.

as compared with the older rocks, they have been studied in far greater detail than any other formation, except perhaps the Coal Measures.

The Age of Reptiles.

The fossils of the Mesozoic period are in general well preserved and abundant, so that the amateur collector will do well to start with some of the beds of this group, if possible, in preference to the beds of the Palæozoic, other than certain of the limestones (Fig. 16).

By the end of Palæozoic time there had been a complete development of invertebrate groups of animals, the highest group, the insects, being fairly abundant fossils in the Coal Measures, and since the Permian no new type of invertebrate has been evolved—every group we now know on the earth has its ancestral representatives in the Palæozoic. The vertebrates had been well established in the Old Red Sandstone lakes, with their abundant fishes, and in the Carboniferous the Amphibia were to be found in the Coal-Measure swamps, and their footprints are common on the sandstones of Permian age. The most productive exposures of these sandstones are at Mansfield, Notts., in a sandstone quarry of Permian age, and at quarries in the Penrith Sandstone, in the Vale of Eden; footprints are also fairly common in the red sandstones of several quarries in Dumfrieshire and near Elgin, both in Scotland. The Mansfield beds are important, as they contain true reptilian footprints in addition to those of numerous amphibia. This is evidence that the reptiles as a group had originated some time prior to the Permian, and there is other evidence to support this conclusion (Fig. 17).

The outstanding feature of life in the Mesozoic is the sudden expansion and complete dominance of reptile life among all the vertebrates. The reptiles found conditions such that they could develop almost without competition and could enter almost every kind of environment. In the Lias a group developed a fully marine habit—the giant fish-lizards, Ichthyosaurus and Pleisiosaurus (Fig. 17, *b*). Ichthyosaurus is a fish-shaped reptile, with a fin on the back, and two pairs of paddles, the front ones placed like the paired pectoral fins of a fish, and the rear ones placed at two-thirds the length of the body from the front. The spinal column is continued as the lower support of a large tail-fin. Pleisiosaurus had a rounder, stouter body, with paddles in similar position, but with a very long, flexible neck carrying the head. The skeletons of these reptiles have been found in great numbers and in fine preservation in the shales of the lower Lias at Lyme Regis, Dorset, at Street, Somerset, at several places near Whitby, Yorks, and in Leicestershire. Flying reptiles are found in all sections of the Mesozoic, and they approximate closely to birds in having wings developed on their front limbs, but the wing-covering is devoid of feathers. The wing is supported by the extension of one finger of the hand and the body and hind limb (Fig. 17, *a*), and is a fine web of skin. Most of the flying reptiles have a heavily toothed mouth and were probably carnivorous. Sometime in the Mesozoic the true birds were evolved, not from the flying reptiles, but from some simpler and remoter reptilian stock, and their fossils are found in rocks of Jurassic age.

The greatest development of reptiles was on land, where some of the largest animals that have ever lived on earth (except perhaps some of the whales) belonged to this group. There is a rough differentiation among them, by habits of feeding. The giant reptiles were mostly herbivorous, massive, slow-moving and sluggish, and depended for survival on a very thick skin heavily armoured with bony knobs or plates. A smaller group was carnivorous, swift moving, lightly built and preyed on the larger animals (Fig. 17, *c*). Of the giants, the main development was in the Jurassic and Cretaceous periods, and principally in northern Asia and America. Brontosaurus, of the American Jurassic (Fig. 17, *d*), was a creature 70 feet long from head to tail, with an estimated weight of about 35 tons. His body is carried on massive legs like those of an elephant, and from it there rises a massive, elongated neck with a tiny head to complete it. The brains of these reptiles were ridiculously small, some creatures with bodies of several tons weight having a brain of only two or three ounces. Their nervous system was very primitive and sluggish, and it is said, with some amount of truth behind the exaggeration, that if a carnivorous enemy had begun to gnaw at the tip of the tail of one of the giant herbivors, he would have had time to get a fairly good meal before the sluggish brain and nerves had warned the giant what was wrong and enabled him to move away. In the Cretaceous there was a fantastic development of bony armour, both in plates and knobs set all over the tough skin and in spikes, spines and shields,

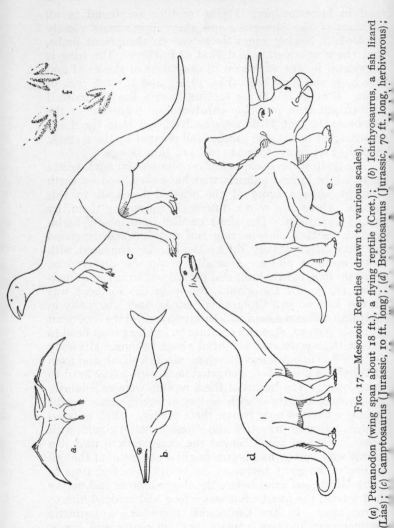

FIG. 17.—Mesozoic Reptiles (drawn to various scales).

(a) Pteranodon (wing span about 18 ft.), a flying reptile (Cret.); (b) Ichthyosaurus, a fish lizard (Lias); (c) Camptosaurus (Jurassic, 10 ft. long); (d) Brontosaurus (Jurassic, 70 ft. long, herbivorous);

over the spine and head. Triceratops (Fig. 17, *e*) developed the largest head in proportion to body of any of the reptiles, and yet in this massive 12-feet-long head there was room only for a few ounces of brain.

The vast change in world conditions at the end of the Mesozoic saw the decline of the reptiles and amphibia, until to-day we have few types left except the frogs, crocodiles and turtles, and the legless snakes. During the Mesozoic there was a small group of reptiles whose remains are found in the Upper Triassic, particularly in Africa in the Karoo sandstones, which from the nature of their teeth are called the Cynodonts, or dog-toothed. These developed along very special lines, and at some point in the Mesozoic there arose from them the first members of the next group that was to dominate the world, the mammals. Teeth and jaws of true mammals are found in certain beds of the Cretaceous, and are evidence that among the giant reptiles that overshadowed the Mesozoic landscape there were already a group of small, rat-like animals, that in the next epoch would entirely supersede them, depending for their dominance on special developments of brain, teeth and feet.

The reptiles in their various forms had adapted themselves to live in the sea, on land and in the air; but their prime distinction from other vertebrates remained true in all cases. The amphibia lay their eggs in water, and their young when hatched are for a time gill-breathers, changing in the adult stage to lung-breathers—changes that can be seen in the development of frog-spawn into tadpole into frog. The reptiles laid their eggs on land, and the young are born as replicas of their parents, air-breathing from the first. In the case of the mammals the young are carried in the mother's womb until their live birth, when they are suckled with milk.

The invertebrate life of the Mesozoic is dominated by the group of Cephalopods (from Greek words meaning head-footed, as the creature progresses with head near the ground and the shell usually held erect above it). The commonest fossils of the period are the Ammonites, univalve shells, coiled in a flat coil, as distinct from the coiled Gastropods, whose shells are coiled around a vertical axis like a screw. The ammonites appear in the Triassic rocks and rapidly expand into countless varieties. The shell is chambered, the animal living in the outer chamber— the body-chamber—and having a connection through all the inner chambers, by which they can be filled with or emptied of water, so allowing the animal to float at the sea surface, or to sink to the bottom to walk about the sea-floor. The Pearly Nautilus is their modern descendant. The internal chambers of the shell are separated by walls of calcite, secreted by the animal, and these partition walls join the outer shell in a convoluted or curly pattern. This inter-section is shown in the fossil as a wavy line, sometimes of extraordinary complexity, running radially from the inner whorl or coil to the outer rim of the shell, like the spokes of a wheel. These wavy lines are called sutures, and are very numerous, and of great use in the classification of the ammonites. The whole group of ammonites shows a com-plete evolution during the Mesozoic, and the stages in this evolution are used to sub-divide the various systems of deposits.

The ammonite group starts with a straight or only slightly curved shell, but rapidly progresses to complete coiling, with each coil just touching the outer edge of the preceding one, like strands of thick rope coiled together. The sutures at this stage are fairly simple, but as evolution proceeds the sutures become more and more complex, and the coils of the shell overlap one another more, so that some of the later forms have the outer coil or whorl almost completely enclosing the inner ones. After the ' acme ' (maximum development) has been passed, the shells lose their power to coil, and the later decadent am-monites are only partially coiled and very irregular. The group becomes almost extinct in the upper Cretaceous.

Other invertebrates include gastropods and pelecypods (the oysters are very abundant in this group, along with forms like the cockle and mussel), a few corals, and the ancestors of the crabs, lobsters and crayfish. Closely allied to the ammonites are the Belemnites, the hard shield part of creatures rather like a cuttle-fish. The animal, like the ammonites, had a head armed with eight tentacles or arms, ranged around the mouth. It had a small number of very small chambers, ranged in a straight series one behind the other, and forming the front end of a long, dart-shaped, solid calcite ' guard '. This is usually the only part left as a fossil, and has long ago been given the fantastic name of the Devil's thunderbolts.

The sea urchins make a most important group in the Jurassic and Cretaceous, and are fairly common fossils; but, being made up of a great number of separate plates of calcite held together in life by the outer skin which covered them, they often drifted apart after the animal died and are found as isolated plates, contributing largely to the bulk of part of the chalk. In the chalk the whole shell is sometimes replaced by flint, and then the plates and their markings are all beautifully distinct.

On land, the Jurassic rocks, particularly the estuarine deposits, carried a rich flora, with many unusual plants among them. The true ferns have appeared, and form a goodly proportion of the plant remains. Along with them are true conifers, and the interesting tree Ginkgoales, which still exists as a survival in parts of Asia, and can occasionally be seen as a greenhouse rarity in this country.

CHAPTER XI

The Tertiary period. Continental Tertiary of South-east England. The Tertiary volcanic province of the north-west. The Tertiary mountains. Evolution of the Mammals. The Quaternary Ice Age. Early Man.

THE rocks of Tertiary age in Britain belong to two most strongly contrasted types and areas that it is possible to imagine. The south-eastern area of Tertiary sediments is restricted to East Anglia and the London and Hampshire basins, where the rocks are mainly thin clays, gravel and incoherent sands and shell-banks, resulting in a low topography of rich agricultural land and heath. In contrast with these is the mountainous and savage scenery of the western islands of Scotland—Mull, Skye, the Inner Hebrides and parts of the adjacent mainland, carved out of thousands of feet of volcanic rocks of Tertiary age. In one area there was a period of quiet river estuaries and shallow sea margins, and in the other a large number of mighty volcanoes putting forth some of the greatest eruptions that this part of the world has ever seen. Each type is still in strong contrast with the preceding Cretaceous sea, with its accumulation of chalk muds and its teeming marine life of ammonites, sea urchins and reptiles. On the margins of the shallow Tertiary lagoons there was an abundant mammalian life in forests, in which many of our existing trees were already present in ancestral form and in which flowering plants had at last appeared.

The Tertiary in most parts of the world is a period of instability and of giant earth movements, the result of which was the elevation of our largest existing mountain ranges, the Alps, Himalayas, Andes and many other of the world's highest mountains. Since Tertiary times there has been very little change in the relative distribution of land and sea and little beyond the first carving up of the landscape under the erosion of modern times.

The Cretaceous period ended with the elevation of the sea-floor into a system of ridges and shallow seas, in which the greater part of Britain was land area, with a sea to the south-east, the shoreline of which spread over south-eastern England and East Anglia. This transition from the Cretaceous to Tertiary conditions must have taken a long time, as everywhere there is a big break between the two formations, and the higher beds of the Cretaceous which are present on some parts of the Continent were eroded away everywhere in Britain. The lower beds of the Tertiary, called the Eocene, rest unconformably on the deeply eroded chalk. The great changes in fauna between the two formations also argues a comparatively long period, for which we have no direct record. In the area between the Tertiary continent of Europe and North Africa there was a wide sea, of which the Mediterranean is but the miserable remnant, in which deposition was continuous from early Mesozoic times. The sediments of that sea were squeezed up and folded into the Alps during the Tertiary, and there some of the intermediate beds are found which are missing in this country. The whole Tertiary is divided into four parts: the Eocene, Oligocene, Miocene and Pliocene, the names being based upon the proportions of extinct and still-living animal types found fossil in them (' Dawn of the recent,' ' few recent ', ' less recent ' and ' more recent ' being approximate meanings of the names). The Eocene opened with a large estuarine area open to the east, in which sands, loams and clays were deposited. The area was subsiding slowly, the sands being followed by the ' London Clay ', which is a true marine clay with a wide range of fossils. The presence of drifted palm trees, crocodiles, sharks, turtles and shells of tropical type indicates a very warm climate. The upper part of the Eocene is a series of sands and clays with fossils which suggest that they were not far from a shoreline, abundant forest debris being drifted out among them. Many present-day sub-tropical trees are here found for the first time, fig, laurel, etc., being fairly common. The Oligocene is found only in the Hampshire Basin, and is there only a thin series of fresh-water clays and marls, thin limestones and sands, mostly deposited in shallow lagoons and representing a very incomplete succession. The earth movements that raised the Alps during the late Oligocene and Miocene were already raising the greater part of Britain into the land area which it still is, and only in East Anglia were any further Tertiary sediments accumulated. There, in a narrow strip near the coast, the estuarine channels of the older and greater river Rhine wandered during the Pliocene over the exposed Eocene land-surface, piling up winding shell-banks and gravel spits, shifting them in the marine area of the delta, leaving them sometimes to be moved by the currents of the North Sea. The chief interest of these beds is their abundance of shells, many of them of types still existing, and the change in proportions between those types which now live in warm seas and those which are of Arctic habit. This evidence will be discussed in the consideration of the Ice Age, the chief event of the next or Quaternary period.

The outstanding event of the continental Tertiary is, of course, the long series of earth movements that culminated in the formation of the Alps, the mountains of central and eastern Spain and some of North Africa, in this part of the world, and in the elevation of the Himalayas and other similar ranges in Asia and in America. In Europe the movement northwards of part of Africa against the fairly rigid block of the Russian platform of Archæan and Palæozoic rocks squeezed up the sediments of a great geosyncline that lay across southern Europe. The high folds so produced were pushed over towards the north, and from their overturned strata the mountains and valleys of the Alps have been carved. Such a great ' earth-storm ' extending through the middle portion of Tertiary time, Oligocene and Miocene, had its reflections over a wide area. Away from the more violent folding gentler ' ripples ' were formed as broad and rather shallow synclines and anticlines, and some of these affected the south of England, folding the lower Tertiary strata and the underlying Mesozoic, making the London Basin and the Hampshire Basin, and completing the folding of the great Weald Anticline. Farther north there was little effect of the folding to be seen, but the period was occupied by violent volcanic outburst and followed by igneous intrusion on a large scale.

The products of these volcanoes have been subjected to deep erosion, both sub-aerial and marine, and much of them has disappeared; but what remains is still impressive. The igneous activity was localised at several centres (see map, Fig. 15, for Tertiary volcanic centres), of which the main are Skye, Rum, Ardnamurchan, Mull, Arran and around the Mourne Mountains in Ireland. The earliest outbursts were widespreading flows of basaltic lava from central cones, the basalts building up nearly horizontal plateaux, of which in Mull there still remains a thickness of 6000 feet, in spite of much denudation. These plateau lavas, fed from innumerable centres not now recognisable, spread over a very wide area, that includes the Faroe Islands, Iceland, Greenland and Jan Mayen Island, so that the areas still to be seen in western Scotland and on the lands just mentioned are at most only a tiny fragment of what were erupted.

A second phase of activity was marked by the formation of large central explosive vents, with more acid lavas, which were followed by the intrusion of plutonic masses. This intrusive phase was partly accompanied by and partly followed by fissuring of the land, mainly in a north-west to south-east direction, and into these fissures, numbering thousands in all, basaltic magma was intruded to form the swarms of dykes that cut the whole of this north-west area, some of which extend south-eastwards as far as the Yorkshire coast. The crater of the central volcano of Mull was approximately six miles in diameter, and, after a period of extrusion of lavas, it became the seat of very complex igneous intrusions. The same story is followed approximately in all the centres of activity. The intrusive rocks include the granite of Mull, the gabbros of Ardnamurchan, the gabbros of the Cuillin Hills of Skye and the granites of the Red Hills; in Arran there is again the massive central boss of granite with Goat Fell carved from it, and in Ireland the granites and gabbros of the Mourne Mountains again provide impressive scenery.

Most of the fossils of the Tertiary are recognisable as the ancestors of existing creatures; there is a distinctly 'modern' look about any assemblage of them. The most important group is that of the Mammals, and among these evolution was rapid. The horses, elephants, deer, cattle, and other now-familiar groups are first recognised by their structure, in small creatures in the Eocene, which change rapidly towards their modern forms. The greatest changes are seen in the structure of the feet and in the growth of the brain, while the teeth change in character at the same time. Teeth and feet are closely allied to the particular life-habits of the group; in the grazing and herbivorous animals teeth are mainly differentiated into a cropping group at the front of the mouth, and grinders for pulping the vegetable food. In many groups the food is swallowed in partly chewed condition and later brought back to be chewed again as a cud; this is characteristic of cattle. In the carnivors the teeth are developed for tearing and cutting flesh and tough skin, and become formidable weapons of attack. As in the case of the reptiles, the carnivorous mammals never developed great size, but depended on speed of attack and lightness of structure combined with great muscular strength. The herbivorous animals developed either great speed, for safety, as among the deer and horses, or large size and thick hides, as in the case of the elephants, rhinoceroses, and hippopotamuses.

The invertebrate fossils are dominated by gastropods and pelecypods, the other groups of shell-fish becoming almost extinct. Corals are restricted to warm seas and to comparatively few varieties. On the land areas forests flourished, in which many modern trees are found, particularly the evergreens, cypress, etc., and the hardwoods, oak, ash, etc. Among the forest undergrowth the flowering plants flourished and rapidly increased in variety. Insect life was abundant, and true birds were to be found everywhere. The climate of Tertiary time can be determined with considerable precision from the number of species of plants and animals whose habits we know from existing specimens. The lower Eocene in Europe contains abundant fossils of temperate plants, but the middle and upper Eocene see a very rapid increase in trees that are now tropical in habit. In the Eocene of the London basin there are many sub-tropical palms, and even a few cacti; but the finest flora is found in the middle Eocene beds of Alum Bay, Isle of Wight, and of Bournemouth. Here more than sixty families of plants have been obtained, which include many species of fig, eucalyptus, araucaria, etc., and trees of definitely tropical habit.

In the Oligocene the plant assemblage is more temperate, but species of flowering plants and shrubs continued to grow far within the Arctic circle. The rest of the Tertiary gives evidence of a progressive cooling of the climate, which culminated in the glacial conditions of the Ice Age in the immediately post-Tertiary period.

The marine fossils of the later Tertiary strata illustrate in striking fashion this progressive cooling. In the Pliocene deposits of East Anglia there are several subdivisions in which the fossils have been examined in relation to existing members of the same groups, and classified as of three types—Southern, Northern, and common to both types of sea. A table of these sub-divisions, with proportions, will be almost self-explanatory.

Name of sub-division, oldest at base.	Southern types, per cent.	Northern types, per cent.	Southern and Northern, per cent.
Weybourn Crag	—	33	56
Norwich Crag	7	32	50
Butley Crag	13	23	47
Newbourne Crag	16	11	36
Walton Crag	20	5	35
Coralline Crag	26	1	31

The uppermost part of the Pliocene consists of fresh-water and estuarine deposits, which include many remains of mammals which throw light on the changing climate. The most abundant of the large mammals are the elephants, the commonest being two species which are of southern type, the deer of many species, bison, hyæna, hippopotamus and rhinoceros, and a number of smaller mammals, all suggestive of a temperate climate. These all became extinct in the Ice Age, and of thirty large land mammals present in the upper Pliocene, only three are now living in Britain or have lived there within the historic period, and only six still exist in any part of the world. This suggests that the sea changed from temperate to Arctic condition earlier than the land climate. The deposits resting on the Pliocene are taken as the base of the Pleistocene (Quaternary), and start with an Arctic plant-bed, in which there is change to Arctic conditions on land as well as in the sea.

Quaternary.

The Quaternary epoch is subdivided into two systems, but these are not well marked, there being no line of clean-cut division between them. The older and greater part of the Quaternary is the Pleistocene, which in the Northern Hemisphere coincides with the Great Ice Age. The upper Quaternary is the Recent, in which we are now living, and is sometimes referred to as post-Glacial.

The Pleistocene period of glacial cold is the natural continuation of conditions that were seen to be in process of development in the Pliocene, and which started some-where in the mid-Tertiary. The lowest Pleistocene is the Arctic Plant-bed of the Norfolk coast, well seen on the fore-shore at Cromer, and already mentioned as containing Arctic plants. In a very early stage of the Pleistocene snow was accumulating over Scandinavia and sending down streams of ice into the North Sea. The cover of ice gradually increased until an extended glacier pushed its way right across the North Sea and piled up against the east coast of Britain, depositing boulder clay (fine rock debris and boulders) along the coast from mid-Durham to Suffolk. Between this boulder clay and the Arctic Plant-bed there is a series of gravels on the Norfolk coast that were probably piled up along the shore by floating ice, and by re-washing

of the Pliocene land surface by streams and rain. Snow
began to accumulate on the higher hills of this country,
and snowfields with glaciers or streams of ice coming out
from them were soon established on the Highlands of
Scotland, the Lake District, Pennine and the Welsh hills.
As these streams increased, the glaciers from them poured
out on to the low-lying plains, and along the east coast
they were able to push the Scandinavian ice-front back into
the North Sea basin. The presence of this Scandinavian
ice-front as a barrier to the east caused the increasing
ice-streams off the Pennines and the Scottish Hills to turn
south and north along the coast, and in some cases to turn
inland again. North of the Firth of Forth, Scottish ice
was constrained to pass northwards along the coast, then
turn north-west across the lowlands of Sutherland and
Caithness, finding free exit in the open sea to the north and
west of Scotland. From the Forth southwards the ice-
streams were turned south along the coast, pressing inland
across the Wash and East Anglia. On the west the Irish
Sea soon became filled with ice, and Lake District and south
Scottish ice was compelled to pass along the west coast,
thrusting inland across the Lancashire and Cheshire plains,
and sending a broad glacier southwards down the lowlands
of western England, south past Birmingham and almost to
Bristol. Each large mountain mass was a centre from which
ice-streams radiated, meeting on the lowlands and moving
on towards the south or to the open sea, where they
eventually melted.

At the maximum extent of glaciation the various ice-
streams were united into one vast ice-sheet, which extended
to a southern edge approximately across the south of England from London to Bristol. South of this there was no
ice-cover, but there was a broad belt over southern England
and across Europe, where the conditions were probably
those of a subarctic tundra. Under these conditions all
the animals of warm and temperate habit were driven
southwards into Africa, and few of them returned after the
Ice Age. The British Isles were from mid-Tertiary times
until long after the Ice Age part of the continental land

area, the English Channel not being then formed, so that animals could migrate between here and the Continent, and between Europe and Africa (the Straits of Gibraltar being post-glacial as well) without any hindrance (Fig. 18).

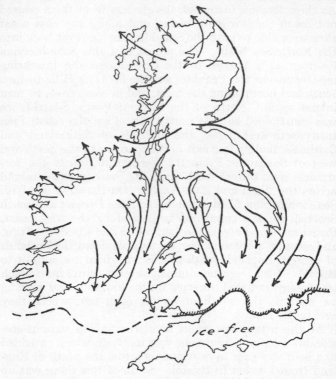

ice-free

FIG. 18.—Lines of Ice-flow and Southern Limit of Ice-sheets. Very much simplified.

The detailed movements of the several ice-streams over the country can be traced by means of ' erratics '—boulders of easily recognised rocks which are limited in their occurrence, which were torn up by the ice and carried in it to some other part of the country before the ice melted. There is a granite which forms part of Shap Fell, Westmorland, which is unlike any other in Britain, and ice from the south of the Lake District carried blocks of this all across the Stainmore Pass over the Pennines, down the Vale of York and along the Yorkshire coast, and across Lincolnshire into the Midland plain. All along that route there are fragments of this granite to be found in the boulder clays. Other fragments were carried from Shap down the Lune valley and across Lancashire and Cheshire. Any boulder clay or glacial gravel must be examined for pebbles that are 'foreign' to the immediate locality; when traced to their source they will give a line of movement of an ice-stream. The rocks over which ice has passed are scratched by the boulders frozen into the under-side of the ice, and the direction of the scratches will supplement the directions deduced from erratics.

The extent of the ice over the country varied from time to time in response to minor changes of climate, and the ice-front showed considerable oscillations, returning after a retreat by a slightly different direction. Thus in one area we may get a succession of different boulder clays. On the East Coast, in most parts, there are at least three different boulder clays, each with different erratics—on the Yorkshire coast anywhere between Spurn Point and Flamborough the three clays are as follows:

3. 'Hessle clay'—erratics mainly Pennine, Northumberland, Cheviot and South Scottish.

2. 'Purple clay'—erratics mainly Pennine, Lake District, and local.

1. 'Basement clay'—erratics mainly Scandinavian.

Such animals as were able to exist in the glacial conditions roamed about the edge of the ice, and during periods of retreat and oscillation of the ice edge were able to inhabit caves which later were again covered with ice debris. In the cave deposits there are many animals preserved which took refuge there in the opening phase of the Ice

Age—animals mainly belonging to the warm, southern group. Cave lion, hyæna, hippopotamus, rhinoceros, and elephants of warm type have all been found in various caves, in Kirkdale Cave, East Yorks; Victoria Cave and Raygill Cave, West Yorks; in some of the Derbyshire caves; in Kent's Cavern near Torquay, and in numerous other sites. In those caves in which any later remains are found these animals have disappeared, and their place is taken by a group adapted to Arctic life. The polar bear, mammoth, woolly rhinoceros, Arctic fox, are among the commonest members of this later group, which only became extinct with the return of warmer conditions at the end of the Ice Age.

The glaciation of the country has had a marked effect on the topography and scenery, which can be studied in any of the hilly regions. The passage of such great sheets of ice, in some places more than 2,000 feet thick, with the underside armed with boulders and rock fragments frozen in, was like the work of a giant rasp or file. All the sharper contours were rounded, crags of rock had the sharp edges taken off, and mountain peaks were given a softer rounded outline. Any of the hills of the Lake District will illustrate this feature: Great Gable, Helvellyn, Skiddaw —all alike have gracefully rounded summits and flanks, broken here and there by the excavation of torrential post-glacial streams, but on the whole presenting large surfaces of fairly smooth slope. The deeper pre-glacial hollows are filled with tightly packed boulder clay and on the lowlands the boulder clay makes a uniform blanket that is almost featureless. The river valleys were deeper before the Ice Age, but were then filled with boulder clay, so that many of our rivers in their lower courses are still re-excavating their channels through these deposits.

As the ice finally melted and the front of the glaciers retreated to the north, many lakes were formed against the hillsides, held up in lateral valleys by the ice. The overflow from these lakes cut channels across the intervening hill-spurs by which they overflowed; but when the ice had gone and the old drainage line was reopened, these

temporary channels were abandoned, and now lie high
and dry in places where no river could ever have cut them.
A few such ' dry valleys ' have been of great importance
to engineers. The railway from Darlington to Newcastle
uses a large ' dry valley ' across the Magnesian Limestone
ridge at Aycliffe, and by it saves a mile or more of deep
cutting or tunnel. Newton Dale in East Yorkshire, between
Malton and Whitby, used by the railway, is another similar
channel. One that has had influence on the river system
is Ironbridge Gorge, the present channel of the River Severn.
At a late stage in the ice retreat a mass of ice across the
Lancashire plain impounded a huge lake between its curved
front and the northern slope of the Welsh Hills, the old
gathering-ground of the pre-glacial River Dee. This lake
overflowed by a low pass near Ironbridge, and before the
ice finally retreated had cut the pass so deep that the
drainage was able to make permanent use of it. The old
course of the Dee is blocked by mounds of boulder clay,
and what were before the Ice Age the upper tributaries of
the Dee are now the head waters of the Severn. This is an
interesting case of ' river capture ' due to glacial interference.

The vast spread of boulder clay over the Midland plain
has provided the material of the brick-making industry,
and brought great fertility to the land. The ice-streams
picked up rock from all the formations over which they
passed, ground the material together to a fine rock-flour,
and so gave an ideal mixture of all rock constituents in the
boulder clay. When the clay has weathered and been
broken down, it gives a good balanced soil.

In mountainous districts the ice-streams descending the
steep mountain valleys were able to ' dig in ' with their
snout in the way that no river can, so that where the valley
slope changes from the steep mountainside to the more
level plain, the valley has been super-deepened for a few
miles, and these hollows, filled with water, have formed the
lakes of the Lake District, Wales, and Scotland. While
glaciation has smoothed off some of the more rugged scenery,
it has atoned for that by providing the lakes so abundantly.
At the end of the glacial period there were lakes in practically

all the Pennine valleys, often several in each valley, one after another, but the silt and gravel washed from the hills by the post-glacial streams have filled them in, and they are now traceable only as dead-level flats of silt, which in winter are often flooded and look more like their original condition than at other times.

The Pleistocene is of vast interest to man, as it was during that period that the human stock came into its own and developed as Man. The anthropoid apes—the main stock to which humans belong—arose during the later Tertiary, and during the Pliocene the direct human ancestors were already living. The stress of the Pleistocene conditions, with the great concentration of mammals along the advancing ice-fronts, provided the stimulus which enabled the pre-Man to become Man, to hunt, and in his hunting to make weapons which for ever separated him from his fellow animals. The weapons soon became tools, and with their making and using, eyesight and brain co-ordinated with hands and fingers, and Man began to depend on brain and tools for survival, rather than on strength and speed. The earlier stages of pre-historic Man are associated with the Ice Age on the Continent and in the Thames valley and the south of England, where his flint implements are found both in caves and in the river-gravels. It was not until late in the Old Stone Age that the more northern parts became sufficiently free of ice for Man to wander or settle there, and over the Pennines and still farther north it was not until the very end of the Old Stone Age (Palæolithic) that the country was freed of ice and snow and provided food for the wandering animals that Man hunted. The account of early Man is thus bound up with the later phases of geology, the Pleistocene and Pliocene; but any detailed study of his tools and habits properly belongs to the subject-matter of Archæology. This is one of the many instances where subjects overlap and can be approached from two different sides.

The fossils of the Pleistocene are mainly those of the cave-dwelling animals, with a few remains of plants and shells from the tundra gravels south of the general glaciation.

After the disappearance of the ice there was a long period of variable climate, cold-wet and warm-dry intervals with some warm-wet periods among them; during these periods peat was formed in some parts, and our present vegetation and animal life made their way back into the country. It was not until after the final disappearance of the ice that Britain was severed from France by the cutting of the Channel, so that migration both of animals and humans was easy in the early post-glacial period.

The story of the geological evolution of this country, as reviewed in the last four chapters, shows very clearly the tendency for geological events to work through a definite order or cycle, which complete cycle is repeated several times. The three major geosynclines are clear—Cambro-Silurian, Carboniferous and Mesozoic—and are separated by arid continental episodes—the Old Red Sandstone, and the Permo-Triassic. There is every evidence that in many parts of the world the late Permian was a period of glaciation with Arctic cold, similar to the glacial period of the Pleistocene which followed the geosyncline of the Tertiary period which was centred over the Mediterranean, but scarcely represented in the rocks of this country. Each geosyncline was terminated by a period of intense pressures and mountain folding, accompanied or followed by igneous activity.

It is surely more than coincidence that all the major events of biological evolution are also associated with these physical cycles. The periods of mountain-building, of instability of the earth's crust, and of difficult climates may have provided the stimulus for great biological experiment. The appearance of all the major groups takes place in these unstable periods. The invertebrates appear in the interval between the pre-Cambrian deposits and the Cambro-Silurian geosyncline; vertebrates are developed at the end of Silurian; the reptiles appear in the Permian; mammals at the end of the Cretaceous, and man at the end of the Tertiary.

These correlations can be displayed most simply in a table as follows :

Age million yr: 1 — 1 20 1 — 70 110 140 180 220 280 310 340 400 500

Geological system.	Biological age.	Principal biological events.	Mountain folding	Conditions.
PLEISTOCENE	Age of MAN	Extinction of the greater mammals	—	Glacial
PLIOCENE MIOCENE OLIGOCENE	Age of MAMMALS and Modern PLANTS	Origin of Man / Acme of mammals / Rise of higher mammals and anthropoid apes	ALPINE	Volcanic area in North West. Land and estuarine in South East
EOCENE				
CRETACEOUS	Age of Giant REPTILES	Extinction of giant reptiles, rise of flowering plants	—	Clear water marine / Geosyncline
JURASSIC		Rise of birds and giant reptiles		Shallow marine
TRIASSIC		Rise of ammonites		Arid desert.
PERMIAN	Age of AMPHIBIA	Extinction of much ancient life	HERCYNIAN	Cold desert
CARBONIFEROUS		Rise of primitive reptiles and insects / Rise of amphibia and of land flora		Geosyncline
DEVONIAN	Age of FISHES	Rise of lung fishes and first air breathers	CALEDONIAN	Mountainous desert
SILURIAN	Age of GRAPTOLITES and TRILOBITES	Rise of corals		Deep geosyncline
ORDOVICIAN CAMBRIAN		First marine faunas		

(handwritten left margin: Quaternary, Tertiary/Cainozoic, Secondary/Mesozoic, Primary/Palaeozoic)

SECTION III. APPLIED GEOLOGY

CHAPTER XII

Applied Geology. Engineering : water supply; underground water; springs; artesian wells; surface water supplies; reservoir sites; landslides.

GEOLOGY finds its greatest applications in the twin pro-fessions of engineering and mining. This is almost in-evitable, as geology deals with the materials of the earth's crust, the engineer selects those materials for his structures, and in the immediate crust has to find suitable foundations for his structures, to tunnel through and excavate in the crust. It is therefore essential that he should have the help of the geologist to inform him of the nature and strength and reactions of different strata, the probable extent of different kinds of ground and materials, and the lines of strength and weakness in any particular piece of ground. The miner is equally concerned with knowing the extent of mineral deposits and understanding the nature of the ground from which they are to be excavated. In both cases there are the two aspects in common: (a) the mineral properties and resources of materials and rocks, and (b) the strength and structure of any part of the crust in which excavations are to be made. The civil engineer, in addition to structures, has many problems concerned with the securing of adequate water supplies on both large and small scale, in which the geologist will have much to say.

Water Supply.

All the water available for man's use at the surface of the earth is taking part in the never-ending cycle of evaporation, storage in cloud, precipitation as rain, and return by springs, streams and rivers to lakes and oceans, to follow round the same cycle again. The water-supply engineer has the task of impounding and using what he needs of this water, during the latter portion of the cycle—that is, between its precipitation as rain and its return to the ocean basins. The water available in any district can never exceed the total rainfall of that area, and in fact will never be more than a fraction of that amount. The first concern, then, must be with available rainfall. Rainfall is affected by the proximity to oceans, the direction of the prevailing wind, the presence of high ground or mountain ranges to secure precipitation, and by the general seasonal characters of the climate. In making any estimate of available water, the mean annual rainfall must be judged where possible from the records of rain-gauges that have been collecting over a long period of years. The British Rainfall Society have long runs of figures for most districts, but these should be supplemented by local figures. From a long run of records the average of the three driest consecutive years recorded should be taken as the probable minimum supply that will ever be available. Of the total rainfall, only a part is available for use. The rain on reaching the ground can be regarded as being disposed in three separate fractions, and these fractions, according to what happens to them, are called (a) the ' evaporation ' fraction, (b) the ' percolation ' fraction, and (c) the ' run-off ' fraction.

(a) *Evaporation.*—Much of the rain that falls finds rest on a non-absorbent or only partly-absorbent surface, and will be subject to evaporation, either by wind or sunshine, or both. Rain falling on the leaves of trees, on grass and vegetation generally, on much of the stony ground, and in hollow water-logged places, is subjected to evaporation before it can run away or soak into the ground. Evaporation goes on continuously from the surface of streams, lakes and reservoirs, and from any area of stagnant water. If rainfall is gentle and spread over long periods, then evaporation will be much greater than when rain is heavy and concentrated. It is very difficult to make an actual measurement of total evaporation, but, after many observations over the greater part of the British Isles, it has been taken as a working rule that approximately one-third of the total rainfall is lost. This figure is not correct, but it is found that evaporation does vary in this country between about 9 inches and 18 inches of rain per annum, according to the total rainfall and the nature of the site. In this matter the engineer's personal judgment will have to be taken.

(b) *Percolation.*—This is the fraction of the rainfall that soaks into the ground, and that may re-emerge on lower levels as springs, or may be tapped in wells or bore-holes. It is therefore of the greatest importance to the geologist seeking underground water. Percolation depends on several factors—the nature of the ground, an open, granular, sandy soil obviously helping percolation, while a stiff, impervious clay will prevent it—the nature of the cover, whether there is a close vegetation turf, underwood that will reduce evaporation and slow down the run-off, so that there is more time for percolation—the slope of the ground, as the rain will run off steep slopes so rapidly that there is little time for percolation, while flat ground allowing water to stand will aid it. All these factors must be examined and counted in forming an estimate of probable percolation.

(c) *Run-off.*—This is a measurable fraction, and consists of the total water discharged by streams and rivers from the area under consideration. This can be measured by making stream gaugings at the points where all streams leave the area, and if the area is not self-contained, gauging the streams entering the area as well, and getting the difference. The difference between total rainfall and run-off is the amount that is shared by evaporation and percolation, and the proportions of this must be estimated before one can get an adequate idea of possible underground water supplies.

The water available may be obtained in two principal ways: either the run-off fraction can be impounded in storage dams and reservoirs, or some of the percolation fraction can be caught by tapping springs, sinking wells or putting down boreholes.

Underground Water Supplies.

The fraction of the rainfall which soaks into the ground by percolation may follow many different courses—some of it is taken up by the roots of plants, some is brought back to the surface by capillary attraction through the pores of the soil and then evaporated from the surface; a large proportion of the water emerges sooner or later as springs, which then enter into the total run-off fraction, while some remains in the pore-spaces of rocks and maintains the ground-water saturation level. The geologist in search of water is chiefly concerned with the saturation water and that moving water which will emerge in springs. The movement of underground water depends on two properties of the rocks making up an area—their porosity and permeability. Porosity is the amount of pore-space between the con-stituent grains of a rock, and is very variable. In chalk the porosity may be as high as 50 per cent., while the same figure is reached in many clays, although in the latter case the pore-spaces are so small individually as to be of no account for the passage of water. Sand has a porosity of about 30 to 35 per cent., and sandstone 10 to 15 per cent. Limestone, slate, shale and other compact sedimentary rocks have a porosity of about 4 or 5 per cent., and the crystalline igneous rocks usually less than 1 per cent. The actual size of the individual pores is, however, far more important than their total amount, as fine pores will be quite impervious to the passage of water, while a few large pores may provide a channel through which a steady flow can be maintained. The capacity to allow water to pass is the permeability of a rock, and this depends not only on the size of the pore-spaces, but also on the frequency and nature of joints and structural lines within the rock mass; thus a well-jointed rock which has only a low porosity may yield a greater flow of water than one of high porosity in which the pore-spaces are minute but abundant, and which has few open joints or bedding planes.

There is a depth below the surface at which the rocks are saturated with water, and the general surface of this saturation level is called the **water-table**.   It is the level at which water will normally stand in wells when not being pumped, and the level below which all excavations will fill with water if left.   The shape of the water-table reflects roughly the topography of the ground surface, the variations, however, being smoothed off.   The water-table rises into hills under surface hills and is depressed in valleys where there is low ground.   The depth to the water-table is greatest under the highest ground, but in valleys the water-table often comes to the surface.   Wherever the water-table intersects the ground surface there will be either standing water, as lakes and ponds, or springs, or overground streams or bogs. Underground water moves down the slopes of the water-table, and between the water-table and the surface is a zone in which percolation water is moving through the fissures and pores of the rocks.

The water-table is subject to seasonal rise and fall, and to slight rise after periods of heavy rain.   The rise is usually largest under watersheds and high ground, so that a well that has been sunk on high ground only as far as the top of the water-table will be subject to considerable fluctuation of water level, and may with a low water-table be dry in some parts of the year.   One sunk well below the general water-table will always have water, provided it is deeper than the minimum summer water-table level. The water-table for an area can be plotted by recording the standing water level in all available wells and excavations, the level of springs, lakes, etc., and then drawing a series of contour lines through all the points of equal level.   When this has been done, the shape of the water-table is seen, and, remembering that water moves down the water-table slopes just as certainly as it does down surface slopes, a well-site can be chosen that will ensure a steady flow of water and a minimum fluctuation of water level with the seasons.   In some conditions a ' perched ' water-table is encountered—that is, a water-table in pervious rocks upheld by a bed of impervious strata below it, although below that again is pervious rock.   This is the case in many areas of chalk strata, where ground-water in the pervious chalk forms a water-table near the surface, resting on a floor of impervious clays, such as the Speeton Clay of Yorkshire, while below the Speeton Clay is a series of sandy and calcareous rocks into which the water would at once run if the barrier were removed. In such a case it is sometimes the misfortune of a person deepening a well or borehole, in the hope of getting more water, to pierce the impervious layer and actually to provide a run-off hole by which the perched water-table can drain into the underlying strata. This has occasionally happened in the deep bores in the London chalk.

Springs.

The general conditions governing the formation and maintenance of a spring of water are that there shall be a permeable stratum so placed with regard to outcrop at the surface that it can receive a constant supply of percolation water, which flows through the stratum along the water-table until a place is reached where the water-table in that stratum intersects the surface of the ground. At that point there is a steady overflow of the water in the form of a spring. The stratum acts as a reservoir and also as a channel for the flow of percolation water. In the simplest case a large bed of gravel or sand resting on impervious clays or shales, having some amount of dip so that the gravels formed a capping to a hill and the impervious floor outcropped on the side of the hill, would provide a spring at the lowest point of the gravel-shale contact. The amount of water coming to the spring would depend on the area of gravel exposed to receive rainfall, the nature of the surface cover of vegetation, that might assist or diminish percolation, and the shape of the beds that might concentrate most of the water at one point or might disperse it to many. A synclinal bed of well-jointed, pervious rock, with a clear and wide outcrop on high ground as collecting area, will have a considerable flow of water along the pitching axis of the fold, and if this intersects a hillside there will probably be copious springs. With a bed of large extent and thickness and great area of outcrop there is likely to be sufficient storage capacity in the rock to maintain a spring through all periods, and one showing little seasonal fluctuation (Fig. 19).

An important factor in the flow of many springs is the occurrence of conditions that will produce an 'artesian' flow. A pervious stratum may dip into the ground in such a way that no part of it reaches the surface where the water within it can escape. The lower part of the stratum

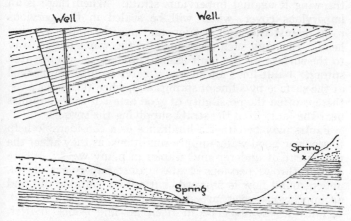

FIG. 19.—Suitable conditions for Springs and Wells.

may be carried to a great depth below the surface, and all its pore and joint spaces be filled with water under pressure of the weight of water above, up to the water-table. When there is an impervious cover sealing in this water under such pressure, a borehole put down through the cover, or a passage for the water being found in some way, the water will rise under the pressure to the height of the normal water-table level at that point, less a small amount due to friction, etc. In the case of the London basin, water falls on the chalk hills of the North Downs and Chilterns, which are the emergent outcrops of a great synclinal basin of chalk strata. The central part of the basin is sealed in with a cover of London Clay and other impervious strata at a level much lower than the water-table level. Where boreholes are put down through the impervious cover to the chalk, the water rises under hydrostatic pressure and flows out at the surface. Such a well is called ' artesian ', after the province of Artois in France, where similar conditions prevail and where such wells first became of general use. Artesian conditions are often produced by faulting. A pervious stratum with a steady dip is cut off in depth by a fault, throwing it against impervious strata. When there is an impervious cover, water will be sealed in the pervious rock against the fault barrier, and may be under artesian head. In many such cases some of the water finds a way to the surface up the fault fissure, producing a deep-seated spring. Fault-lines are in many cases seen to be marked at the surface by a line of springs and, when this is the case, there is often the possibility of good artesian water supplies near the fault from the strata supplying the springs.

Faults may be either a hindrance or a considerable help to securing good water-supply conditions, as they affect the movement of underground waters in many ways. Where a fault throws pervious strata against impervious strata, underground flow is stopped, but with a suitable dip and an impervious cover, artesian conditions are often formed. A fault fissure may be in itself an impervious barrier, if the rock debris broken along the fault plane is compacted with shale or clay materials, and in this case the fault may be a completely water-tight barrier between two water-bearing areas. On the other hand, a fault which traverses some hard sandstone rocks may be filled with a very open and pervious breccia, which will form an ideal channel for the movement of water. In deciding the position of a bore-hole in relation to a fault, the nature of the fault fissure should be explored, and the conditions so investigated as to know whether to preserve the fault as the barrier holding up an artesian supply, or to cut it in order to tap resources of water that are draining along its course. Every case must be examined locally, as no general rule can be given that will hold in all cases.

The quality of underground water is easily affected by the nature and structure of the rocks from which it is obtained. The saturation and percolation water will take into solution small quantities of soluble minerals present in the rocks. In the rocks of the Permian and Triassic strata there are many beds of rock-salt and gypsum, and wells and bore-holes may provide water having these salts in solution. Water that has percolated through strata containing iron pyrites or other iron salts may be heavily charged with iron oxides resulting from their decomposition, the so-called ' ochre-water ' often associated with springs near a heather moor region being such waters charged with iron oxides leached out of the ' iron-pan ' that forms at the base of peaty soils.

Sand forms a natural filtrant for water, and passage through a sand-filter can often make otherwise unsafe water quite usable. Where water is obtained from sand-stones there is usually sufficient natural filtration to give entirely safe water, but in limestone areas, where most of the underground water runs in open channels and solution passages, there is no such filtration, and any pollution will remain unfiltered, and so make the water unsafe. The value of natural filtration can be exemplified in an interesting case that happened some years ago. The water supply of a village became seriously contaminated, with the outbreak of epidemic disease following this. The water was drawn from shallow wells in a perched water-table. As a temporary expedient, the wells were deepened till the floor of the perched water-table was pierced, and the contaminated water was allowed to drain through into an underlying formation of sandy strata. At a short distance a new well was sunk in this lower stratum, and the water drawn by heavy pumping through the sandy rock. The passage through the intervening sandy strata between the old wells and the new was entirely sufficient to filter the water and make it safe. Water in a fault fissure should be carefully examined, to see whether it is naturally filtered or not.

The relative hardness or softness of natural water is an important consideration that may call for correction, but this is primarily the concern of the water engineer. It is of geological interest to mention the naturally hard waters of the chalk and limestone formations, the iron- or salt-impregnated water of the Permian, and the peaty-coloured water that comes from many of the sandstone moors. The deep brown colour is due to the presence of humic acids in the water, and is to be carefully watched and corrected, as the humic acid is lead solvent. Iron service-pipes and iron pans are safest for use in a district where peaty water is at all prevalent. In some cases such waters are partly neutralised by being run or cascaded over limestone steps and terraces.

Contamination of water drawn from wells and boreholes is often made possible by the nature of the surrounding strata, and these possibilities must be guarded against by the geologist. The plotting of the water-table contours, along with the careful investigation of the dip of rocks and the direction of prevalent joints, should enable the well-site to be chosen in such a line that there is no possible drainage from farmyard or cess-pool into the area drawn upon by the well. Glacial deposits are often very dangerous in this connection, as they are generally impervious, but with many irregular channels of gravel and open sand through them. Cess-pools and septic tanks built in such deposits often have a soak-away that may wander in almost any direction through such a channel and be intersected by a well-feeder. The utmost care must be taken, in such irregular deposits, to verify the feed-line of a well-site. A frequent source of pollution in rural areas is found where a spring is fed to a trough for the use of sheep and cattle, the overflow being trampled to a quagmire by the drinking animals and heavily charged with manure. The soak-away from this overflow then makes its way underground, and may feed to a farmyard pump for human use. A study of the water-table contours and movement of the water would enable an ' upstream ' site to be chosen for the well, which would avoid the worst of the contamination. In all cases it is wise to take a site where the maximum of natural filtration is secured.

Surface Water Supplies.

In the utilisation of the run-off fraction of rainfall, the engineer's problem is to choose a site where, by the construction of as short a dam as possible, he can impound and store as large a volume of water as possible. This choice of site will be made largely on topographical grounds—to secure a large deep valley that can be closed by a short dam, and that will have to feed it as much 'gathering ground' as possible. The site so chosen must then be checked by the geologist, as it needs to be watertight, and structurally capable of carrying the great weight and pressures involved in a reservoir dam. The watertightness will be affected by the porosity of the rocks of the area, the nature of their joints and the presence of faults or folds and their general structure. A valley may be of very promising shape for a reservoir site, and yet if the bounding hills are traversed by beds of porous rock outcropping anywhere below the top water level and passing through the hillsides, either into adjacent valleys or down the valley to below the dam position, with a dip that is away from the reservoir, they will act as a direct channel for escape of the water out of the valley through the hills or around the end of the dam. In some such cases the valley sides are plastered with boulder clay, and if this is sound, it may seal off such rock outcrops; but the closest examination and care are necessary before such a deposit can be relied upon. A valley that is formed along the crest of, or crossed by, an anticline including porous rocks is a most unlikely site for a dam. The rocks along a valley floor are often badly fissured and crumpled, and weathering may extend to a great depth. These conditions are always explored by deep trial trenches and boreholes, and if a site is finally chosen, then the 'puddle-trench' or impervious core of the dam is cut down through the valley bottom until entirely tight and sound strata are reached. This core is also carried laterally into the valley sides to form wing trenches, cutting through all the weathered rocks into the sound core of the hills. Where rocks are very open-jointed, as in coarse sandstones, limestones or some igneous rocks, the task of closing puddle and wing trenches and making the valley floor tight with puddle may be altogether prohibitive. In many cases, however, joints are much closer and tighter in depth, and a deep puddle-trench may cut off all escape along the valley bottom, and wing trenches make the hillsides safe.

Faults can be a determining factor in a dam site; a fault crossing a valley near the proposed site may either make foundations insecure, by the shattered belt of rock near it, may act as a channel for escape of water in depth, or may in a rare case seal off some otherwise pervious stratum and make a site usable. A fault is chiefly to be feared as a bad foundation, faults usually being subject to slight movement or shake in response to earthquake tremors, and so liable to crack any heavy structure carried over them. In a valley cut in folded strata a structure in which the rocks generally dip inwards towards the valley is likely to be a watertight site; where the rocks dip outwards it is most likely that there will be ways of escape for the water. Similarly, an upstream dip is much to be preferred to a downstream dip, both for watertightness and stability. Landslip features are a sure sign of difficulty, as most landslips are lubricated by underground water seepages, and the material is constantly slipping upon these lubricated planes. A mass of landslip rock may thus partly close a valley and make a temptingly narrow site for a dam, but it is very rare indeed to find landslip that will hold water. The danger of leakage as well as the general instability of the material make it necessary to avoid all such sites. At the Broomhead Reservoir for Sheffield landslips were a cause of great increase in cost; when the reservoir was filled within 20 feet of top water level there was leakage of water through landslip material, to the extent of nearly two and a half million gallons a day, and there were many signs of movement along the slips. The condition was remedied and made safe by extremely fine engineering work, but at an additional cost of nearly a quarter of a million pounds.

One of the greatest problems in the construction of a dam, either of earth or masonry, is to get a watertight seal into the valley bottom, along with stable foundations. This is made very difficult because in nearly all deep valleys the actual floor is affected by considerable ' creep '. The softer strata seem to ' give ' and crumple up in the middle under the weight of the adjacent hillsides. There is some amount of movement or squeezing out from the sides, and the whole strata, often to great depth, is opened, its joints and bedding planes being opened and new fractures appearing. Such valley-bottom creep has been found to great depth in the Langsett Reservoir, near Sheffield, where it extended to 120 feet below the valley floor. At the Derwent Valley Dams, Derbyshire, crumpling of the valley-bottom strata went down for nearly 100 feet, and the strata in the hillsides were traversed by innumerable fine slip planes and cracks, inclining in towards the valley bottom and necessitating a great length of wing-trenches to make the site secure. Such crumpling of the floor material is commonest in shales and thin bedded strata, and is nothing like so prevalent in massive rocks.

Glacial phenomena are often a source of trouble, and as most of this country has been heavily glaciated, the geologist must be on the watch for signs of glaciation and ready to explore the nature and extent of glacial deposits. The irregular nature of boulder clay has already been mentioned. Many glaciated valleys have their contours rounded off and smoothed by glacial packing, and the present floor is often traversed by deep drift-filled, ancient channels. For some time before and during the Ice Age, the general level of this country was much higher, in relation to sea level, than it is now, and the vastly enlarged rivers of meltwater were enabled to cut deep channels, sometimes even below present sea level. These old channels are now drift- and gravel-filled, and may constitute a real problem in constructional work. Many of the river estuaries of this country have these buried channels sometimes extending to nearly 190 feet below present sea level. In the upland valleys usually selected for reservoir sites the buried channels are much less than this, and are usually deep, narrow gorges, not necessarily on the present stream-line, but away to one side under a hill-slope that is itself only boulder clay-pack. Thus a dam may cross a present valley floor, founded in tight boulder clay or even in rock, and yet have, at greater depth and to one side, a deep channel partly filled with sand and gravel, and providing a perfect escape for water. The Llannefydd reservoir site in Wales showed a thickness of boulder clay over the whole valley floor to about 13 feet, but when close-set trial pits were made, it was soon found that in one part there was a deep channel of open gravel which necessitated the foundations being taken down in that part to 122 feet. In such glaciated areas the weathering of valley-floor rocks often penetrates to a very great depth and only the closest trials will give a safe picture of conditions. In the case of the Silent Valley scheme, Co. Down, Ulster, trial bores were made along a line of sites across the valley floor. The bores were carried through weathered granite and clay into solid granite at depths down to 50 feet. On the expectation of a sound floor at that depth, work was commenced, and £400,000 spent before it was realised that most of the trial boreholes had gone into large granite boulders in the boulder clay, and not into solid rock. Deep excavation showed the floor to be weathered and filled with drift and gravels to a depth of 180 feet, and a sound dam was made only at a fabulous cost of material and labour. Had the boreholes been supplemented by numerous deep trial trenches, the mistake would not have been made, and a more suitable site would have been chosen.

Many heavily glaciated valleys are scooped out into deep rock-pools, now occupied by lakes or by lake-silts. The steep glaciers coming from the valley head have considerable ' digging ' power as they meet the flattening valley slope in its lower reaches, and may excavate a considerable part of the valley, then rise over a slight rock-bar. All the solid floor is covered by boulder clay and glacial and alluvial debris. In the case of the Vyrnwy Reservoir in North Wales, the engineer in charge recognised the heavy glacial moulding of the valley, and suspecting the possibility of such a buried rock-bar, sought for it by an extensive series of bores and trenches. Such a bar was found, and used as the foundation for the masonry dam, giving perfect stability and safety with shallow foundations. The siting on this ridge is estimated to have saved three to four hundred thousand pounds, as compared with sites within 200 yards of the one chosen.

For the geologist who intends to apply his science in the problems of engineering, every conceivable opportunity must be taken of examining deep excavations, and where any question may arise of foundations for massive structures, only open trial-trenches and shafts, supplemented by many borings should be accepted as evidence. A few hundred pounds spent in exploration of a site may make a difference of many thousands of pounds in constructional cost and all the difference between safety and disaster in the completed work.

Landslips.

Wherever there are deep, steep-sided valleys or natural cliffs, or deep-sided excavations into the crust of the earth, there is danger of landslides being formed. Landslides are of many varieties, from the slight creeps of surface soil seen on many hill-slopes, to the vast areas of cliff and undercliff such as the area of slipped cliff between Folkestone and Dover, involving millions of tons of rock. All landslips, however, can be treated as examples of one or other of three general cases: (a) gravity slides, where a mass of more or less incoherent soil or clay, heavily saturated with water, forms a mud stream and flows under gravity down a hill slope; (b) bedding plane slides, where a series of inclined strata, under the stimulus of continued vibration, earthquake tremor, or undue lubrication of the plane on which it rests, slides forward down the dip at a free edge; (c) structural break, where the strata at the foot of a cliff or steep bank fail under the pressure of the overlying rock, and shearing takes place along a curved plane, followed by downward and forward movement on the shear-plane.

In all cases it seems clear that the essential condition before movement can take place is the complete saturation of the rocks along the plane of movement.

(a) Gravity slides are common where a thickness of boulder clay or other structurally weak rock is cut into a high cliff face, by erosion, either of the sea or streams, or in artificial cut. The high boulder-clay cliffs of East Anglia and of South-east Yorkshire are subject to constant sliding. The clay and sand become completely water soaked in a wet season, the surface forms a mud-stream and flows in a slow river, often reducing the coherence on the cliff front. The clay flows out, cutting back circular-headed gullies, which in turn give rise to lateral flows down their sides. A similar action is seen on steep valley sides, where a cover of boulder clay or of soil and weathered rock debris becomes partly liquified by saturation with rain-water. The soil begins to creep, and rapidly forms a mud-slide, which for the time being relieves the hillside of its accumulated water, the debris dries out, and stability follows for a while. This type of slide is common wherever pervious rocks that are not very strong overlie impervious strata on a slope. The mass of material involved in the slide flows as a viscous mud.

(b) Where a series of rocks is dipping at a moderate angle towards a free edge or cliff face, the rocks in the upper part will remain in position only so long as the angle of slope of the bedding planes is less than the angle of limiting friction and so long as there is cohesion and frictional grip between the rock surfaces. Where the angle of dip approaches the angle of limiting friction, a thin layer of clay or shale rock lubricated by percolating water may completely upset the equilibrium, by lowering the angle of limiting friction for the two surfaces below the actual angle of dip. When that occurs, the upper rocks will slide forward along the lubricated surface. The extent and frequency of land-slides in such a case will be influenced by the closeness and completeness of the system of joints in the rock and the nature of the impervious sliding plane stratum. Where a rock is cohesive with few and ill-defined joints, there are likely to be large slips at rare intervals, but where the rock is abundantly and open jointed, slips will be constant and of small extent, erosion cutting such a cliff rapidly back.

(c) Where rocks are strong enough to be cut into high cliffs, as some sea cliffs on our coasts—for example, the cliffs of Moher in County Clare—which reach 600 feet in sheer height, the pressure of the rock exerted at the toe of the cliff face may cause shearing of the rock, the shear-plane extending in a curve which emerges at the upper surface nearly vertically, and which at the toe is flattened to nearly horizontal. As such a shear-plane forms, it will catch surface drainage water and intercept underground waters, which in time will lubricate it until slipping takes place. When this happens, the big curved wedge above the shear-plane moves with a certain amount of rotation—the toe moves outwards and possibly a little up, and the top slides down and tilts back down the curve. Usually such movement is not very great; sooner or later a second curved slice breaks and moves a little farther back, and a series of curved wedges is accumulated, bringing the cliff material down and forward. In all cases the toe of the slide tends to rise or buckle up at the front, so that there is a crescentic area immediately in front of the slide, where there is vertical disruption and movement. In some cases weaker strata may shear or squeeze under the pressure of overburden, and a certain amount of flow deformation take place, with a general lowering of the upper surface of the whole cliff.

In all cases it is evident that the final determining factor in the landslip is lubrication by percolating water, and the contribution of the geologist is to recognise possible landslip conditions and, if preventive measures are advisable, then to concentrate on complete and adequate interception of ground-water and perfect drainage of the potential landslip surface. An example of each kind will perhaps make the matter clearer. (a) In the course of a large water-supply scheme, in Yorkshire, a distributing tank—that is, a large concrete reservoir of several million gallons capacity—was built upon a hillside overlooking the town to be supplied. A shelf was cut into the hillside, the back portion of which was in Millstone Grit shales, sound, tight ground, and the forward portion in tough, watertight boulder clay. Soon after the tank was filled, movement of the hillside began, which first showed by the rucking up of ground at the foot of the slope, and then by the cracking of the front part of the tank, and escape of its water. It was found, by numerous deep excavations, that at the contact of the boulder clay and the shale slope there was a thin stratum of an inch or so of fine sand. After the tank was completed, the drainage from a duck-pond on higher ground had found its way over the clay surface to a spot where part of this sand layer outcropped, and had soaked away into it. In the course of a few months it had so lubricated the shale–clay surface that a gravity creep of the hillslope clay cover took place, dragging with it and breaking the front wall of the tank which was well founded in the clay. (b) Examples of this type are seen in many road and rail cuttings made in the side of hills with strata steeply dipping in the same direction as the hill slope. On the up-dip side the strata have to be scarped back right to the true dip of the rock, if such slide is to be avoided. On the down-dip side the cutting can be left vertical, as any movement will be away from the track. (c) The great landslip area near Folkestone already mentioned is a case in point, or such a case as the Marine Drive at Scarborough, where the weight of the Castle Hill, with its massive oolite rocks in the upper part resting on a lower portion of Oxford Clay, cut off from the main land-mass by the big faults that run between Castle Hill and the town, has occasionally shown squeezing effects along the foreshore under the Marine Drive. The foundation of the Drive showed a tendency to 'lift' in the toe of an incipient slide, until adequate drainage precautions were taken, and the whole structure made perfectly safe in that way. In deep excavations and in mining, special precautions are needed to counter the shearing and crushing tendency of rocks that are cut under a great overburden pressure. Some of these will be mentioned in connection with mining.

CHAPTER XIII

Engineering problems: Tunnelling. Materials: building-stones; bricks and artificial stone; refractory materials; cements and limes.

Tunnelling.

THE geologist is frequently called upon to give his help in the planning of tunnelling operations, as, from the very nature and methods of his work, it is his job to understand and investigate the properties and structures of the crust to a considerable depth below the exposed surface. By careful mapping at the surface, folds, faults and dipping strata are detected, and their extension in depth and direction can be predicted. When a line along which it is desired to bore a tunnel has been selected, the geologist will, from detailed surface mapping and a few trial pits, give a description of the different rocks likely to be encountered on the suggested line, their structure, whether horizontal or steeply inclined, much or little jointed, whether likely to be found full of water or comparatively dry. He can give information of the behaviour of certain rocks under the pressure of a great depth of cover, and knows much of their properties that will determine their response to drilling and blasting. On his forecasts, the engineer concerned with the driving can anticipate difficulties, prepare for them in his estimates and can have some idea of the material to be excavated.

In a tunnel that was required to pass through a watershed, between a valley where a large reservoir was being built and the valley where the water was to be used, the geologist who was consulted was asked to advise on such a line for the tunnel as would (a) afford a safe, clean-standing tunnel with the minimum requirement of linings and internal support, (b) be as water-tight as possible both during the driving and when in use, (c) in the cutting, produce as much as possible of good-quality, reliable material that could be used in various constructions about the scheme, and (d) be as short a line as possible, consistent with these requirements.

One of the great difficulties in driving a tunnel is to prevent collapse of a bad roof during driving—that is, to find a line in strong strata that can be excavated without too much danger and excessive timbering, and to get a line which will avoid disastrous flooding. In the tunnel under the Mersey recently constructed there was the very grave problem of securing a safe roof-cover and also of avoiding disastrous flooding during the driving and excessive pumping on completion. Like most of the large rivers of this country, the Mersey, during the Ice Age, had parts of its bed deepened to considerably below present sea level. In one place the sub-glacial buried channel of the river is known to extend to 110 feet below present sea level. The greater part of the tunnel was planned to be cut in the rock formation of the Bunter Pebble Beds, a hard brown sandstone, which is, however, one of the best water-bearing formations in this country. The geological problem was to decide how a tunnel could be driven at a suitable depth to lie within this strong Bunter sandstone—which was necessary for structural reasons—and at the same time to miss cutting the gravel-filled and water-logged sub-glacial channel. Also, how far would the Bunter sandstones be themselves water-logged, and liable to flood the workings? The gradient of the approach tunnels from each bank was fixed in the conditions of the Parliamentary sanction, and therefore the depth of the main part of the tunnel would affect the length of these approaches very seriously. Knowing the geological problems and probable conditions, a suitable line was chosen, and a method of driving with a bottom advance heading always from 60 to 200 feet in advance of the main heading, with boreholes put forward and upward at small angles for another 60 to 100 feet in advance of workings, was adopted. Working with special precautions in the areas where the geologist anticipated troubled ground, the driving was made in safety. The sub-glacial channel was cut, but the clay cover overlying the gravel, along with the precautions that were taken and the special lining materials, timbering and pumping arrangements all ready for instant use, enabled the tunnel to go forward through this area with safety and satisfaction. Without the geological knowledge, the fine engineering skill would have been just as handicapped as the geologist would have been without the engineer.

In the Haweswater Reservoir tunnel, through part of the Lake District fells, the mapping of the geologists proved the highly folded character of the rocks—a vast series of lavas and igneous rocks—and enabled a structural section along the line of the tunnel to be prepared. This proved very close to the actual rocks encountered, and enabled considerable advance preparations to be made to encounter particular difficulties. In the Lochaber tunnel of the British Aluminium Co.'s hydro-electric scheme, near Ben Nevis, the tunnel is driven through 15 miles of country largely made up of metamorphic rocks, mica schists and some granite masses. The behaviour of the schists, their direction of bedding, structural lines, etc., were mapped along the surface, and many lines of shattered rock, which proved real difficulties in the construction of the tunnel, were mapped on the surface, and their position in the tunnel predicted, allowing adequate preparations to be made in advance to deal with them.

From these few examples it will be seen that in tunnelling, the geologist can make a definite contribution to the engineer's planning of the work, by giving information on the following points:

(a) The nature of different rocks likely to be cut;

(b) The structure and dip of the rocks, and the existence of particular structures that will need special treatment;

(c) The strength of the material being cut through;

(d) The likelihood of water, its probable amount and most likely places where it will be met;

(e) Peculiar local geological conditions that may cause special difficulties or dangers.

From his wide experience of the rocks of various geological formations, seen both in quarries, cuttings and mines, under many different conditions of weathering, etc., the geologist can often suggest ways of dealing with particular rock types as they are encountered in the cutting. It is common practice now for a geologist to watch the progress of deep tunnel works, almost from day to day, and give the benefit of his knowledge as points relating to rocks and rock structures crop up.

Materials.

Building-Stones.

The quality of a building-stone depends on several different factors that may vary according to the purpose for which the stone is wanted. Durability, colour, resistance to frost and weathering by city atmosphere and the cost and possibility of getting large pieces are the principal considerations. Durability will depend not only on the chemical composition of the rock, but also on the physical structure and the composition of its component parts, particularly the cement between the grains of a granular rock. In igneous rocks such as granites and syenites, which are commonly used for building purposes, the most likely source of failure will be the felspars, which under certain conditions of weathering will break down very easily with the production of clay decomposition products along the cleavage planes. The strength of the rock in compression will be affected by its geological history; a period of folding or faulting movements may have produced microscopic shear-planes and lines of strain all through some or all of the mineral crystals and cause the rock to fail under what would otherwise be a normal loading. Metamorphic rocks such as schists and gneisses are almost invariably full of these strain cleavages, and should rarely be used except for light loaded positions or for ornament. In all cases the examination of thin sections under the microscope will reveal the internal condition of the rock.

In the case of sedimentary rocks, particularly sandstones, the chief concern will be the nature of the cementing material between the silica grains. This will often prove to be weaker than the grains themselves, and failure of the rock will usually be caused by failure of the cement. The cement may have little mechanical strength, in which case it is important to see, again by microscopic examination, what is the distribution of the cement, whether it is present in very fine films between grains, filling coarse interstitial spaces, or irregularly distributed, etc. One must judge from this examination whether the cement will take much or little of the effective load on the rock. The cement may be either very soluble in rain-water, such as the calcareous cements, or it may be liable to chemical decomposition under weathering, such as the common cement, iron carbonate, which can easily break down into iron oxides which will crumble with practically no strength. The reaction of the cement to air must be studied, as in some rocks the cement on exposure soon hardens into an almost watertight skin, which may or may not be an advantage, according to the position of the stone in a building. The relation of the cement to the size and nature of the grains will influence the texture and colour of the rock, and this may be an important factor when choosing a rock for a public building. In a sandstone that has some of its pore space open, or with a cement that will absorb water, there will be some danger of frost-splitting unless the stone is wisely used.

The porosity of a building-stone will have great bearing on its weathering, as frost may act on the enclosed water and break out the grains near the surface; again, a porous stone may absorb rain water and enable it to attack the cement to some depth within the outer surface. On the other hand, a suitably porous rock may by its capillary action bring water from within a wall to the surface, where it can evaporate, and so will secure a permanently dry building. In this case it is essential that the mortar used between the stones is itself not too impervious, or it may prevent such movement and drying out.

A common failure of building-stones in towns, particularly applying to sandstones and limestones, is that which shows as ' scabbing ' and peeling off of surface blisters. This may be due to either of two causes. The atmosphere of most towns contains a small proportion of sulphuric acid, derived by the rain from the sulphur fumes from burning coal, and this acid will attack certain types of cementing material in stones, converting the immediate surface skin from a carbonate form to a sulphate. This chemical change is accompanied by the formation of a hard, impermeable surface skin made up of calcium sulphite and sulphate, which by its crystallisation expands and breaks free from the face of the stone as a blister. Exfoliation of this kind can proceed very rapidly when once it starts, and is particularly severe on the magnesian limestones, such as were used in York Minster (where the atmosphere is not sufficiently bad to do rapid damage) and in the Houses of Parliament, where decay was proceeding at a great rate. Portland Stone, which is used so widely in London for its fine texture and beautiful colour, is also very liable to exfoliation and blistering in a sulphurous atmosphere. Where a stone is exposed to the constant washing action of rain, the production of a skin is prevented, as both sulphite and sulphate salts are easily soluble in water. The blistering is therefore to be guarded against in sheltered parts of a building, under deep cornices, in recesses and undercut parts where rain does not beat freely on the stone. In a building where such conditions are common, it is wise to select a stone with a siliceous cement, or one not liable to sulphate blistering.

Many unsightly buildings owe their defects to the unskilled use of the stone. Much of the durability as well as the attractiveness of stone in building depends on the skill and care with which it is quarried, handled and laid. In sedimentary rocks, which are built up of materials deposited in layers, it is essential that blocks used in a building should lie the same way as they were in the quarry. The bedding planes are the base, the two joint systems form the sides, and a second bedding plane the top of a roughly rectangular lump of stone, in its natural position in the quarry. In good quarrying, this position is marked before a block is 'got', and in all subsequent shaping and dressing this position will be kept in mind. When laid in a building, it should rest upon the basal bedding plane, with bedding horizontal. The reason for this is that in all sedimentary rocks there is a slight variation in the grade of the grains and possibly in the cement, from bed to bed, and the strength of the rock is greater across the bed than with it. If a rock will split at all, it will be along the bedding direction. With a block of stone cut with one side in the natural bedding, forming a 'face', the four sides at right angles to that will be 'end' and 'edge'. Now, if the stone is laid in a wall resting on 'end', with its face vertical, the 'grain' or face may run parallel with the face of the wall, or at right angles to it, going into the wall. In the first case— so-called 'face' bedding (often used by inconsiderate builders as an easy way of securing a smooth finish)—water will get behind the outermost 'face' layer of grains, and sooner or later, in response to temperature and frost, the face layer, possibly only a fraction of an inch thick, will scale off. If there is any grain at all in the stone, this is inevitable In the case of the stone laid with its 'end' in the wall-face and the bed running into the wall but vertical, there will be a constant passage of water along the bed, into the wall and also vertically. If there is any variation in the grade of the different minute layers, those with slightly larger grains or a more friable cement will form capillary channels up which water will be sucked with the greatest ease. Several courses of edge-laid stone may prove an active water channel, drawing ground-water up into the substance of the wall and ensuring a damp building

When a stone is laid on 'bed' with its bedding in the natural position, there is no possibility of scaling off along the face, there will be no passage of water across the grain—that is, vertically up the wall—and any texture lines that develop on weathering will be horizontal and will look æsthetically right. The stone will also be in its position of greatest strength, and not liable to fail by splitting, as is the case in edge-laid stones.

When stone is got in the quarry, it contains what is called ' quarry sap '—that is, a certain amount of inherent water. Most stone hardens appreciably as the quarry sap dries out, and it is therefore an advantage, from a labour point of view, to shape stone as soon as possible after getting, than to allow it to season for a period to get rid of the sap. Green stone—that is, stone still containing the quarry sap—is more liable to frost destruction than seasoned stone, and in other ways as well most stones are improved by careful seasoning. The actual getting in the quarry is important; the use of blasting in heavy charges frequently sets up minute cracks, visible only under the microscope, but still permitting the entry of water and leading to weakness under load. Stone which has been bruised in tooling, say by unskilled use of a heavy blunt tool, frequently develops ' scaling ' spots where bruised. This decay rarely proceeds to any great depth in the stone, but can be sufficient to spoil the surface texture completely. Carelessly operated dressing-machines can cause similar decay of surface, again by slight bruising, but the results of careful experiments suggest that skilful machining with sharp and suitable tools and correct pressure has no deleterious effect on the stone.

Building-stones occur at many geological horizons, and each group has its own well-known character. The Millstone Grit provides massive ' ashlar '—stones that can be got in lumps of a yard cube or even more, of very even grain in all directions and suitable for dock and harbour works and heavy constructional foundation work of all kinds. The Coal-Measure sandstones include many ' freestones '—beds that are very even-grained—so that the stone cuts equally well in all directions and is eminently suitable for carved work. Along with the freestones are many beds of flags, both coarse, thick flags for floors and pavements and finer flags for roofing-slate. The Old Red Sandstone provides some famous flags as well as a good-quality building-stone. The Permian has the Magnesian Limestone, a good ' freestone ' used extensively for the carved work of

Gothic buildings, but liable to deterioration in town atmospheres. The red sandstones of Permian and Trias are an attractive rock, and, in the best qualities, very durable. In the Mesozoic strata there are several fine stones, such as the Bath Oolite, the Cotswold stones, the fine limestones of the Calcareous Grit series, and others, like the Portland Stone and the Purbeck Marble.

Among igneous rocks, the granites of Shap and Aberdeen are best known, with syenites from Peterhead, but most of those used in this country come from abroad. There are fine slates from the Cambrian of Wales, and from the volcanic ashes of Ordovician age in the Lake District.

Bricks and Clay.

After coal, brick clays come probably the second in place of all the mineral productions of Britain, measured both by bulk and value. Clays taken as a very general group are aluminium hydrate and silicate mixtures in various proportions, with a large variety of impurities present in greater or less quantity. The term ' clay ' is so wide that there is an almost infinite variety of substances within its general definition. In this section we shall deal only with those clays used for the manufacture of bricks, pottery and ' refractory ' materials. The essential properties of clay are two: that when mixed with a certain proportion of water it makes a plastic material that can be moulded, and that when baked under certain conditions of temperature and time it becomes hard and durable. The first property is ' plasticity ', and this is the most important. Clays are often spoken of as being ' fat ' or ' lean ', according as they stick together when moulded in a plastic state when they are ' fat ', or tend to be friable and difficult to mould into a shape that will stand firmly when they are ' lean '. Fat clays on being baked shrink considerably in volume, and much of the shrinking is in the form of localised and internal cracks produced on cooling. These render a fat clay of little value for brick-making, where a homogeneous, strong product is required. A lean clay can be moulded sufficiently for making a brick, and when baked, will have little shrinkage and little danger of internal cracks and flaws. Consequently, in selecting a clay for brick-making, the plasticity need be no more than the minimum necessary to ensure successful moulding of the bricks, and the greater the leanness that can be secured along with this, the better will be the strength and quality secured on burning.

A second quality that is important is the ' refractoriness ' of the baked brick. The temperature at which the clay begins to soften and lose shape, or the materials of it begin to fuse, is a measure of this. If the clay has a very high fusion or softening point, then it may be regarded as a ' refractory ', and used for making fire-bricks and furnace linings, etc. These will be described later. This property is influenced by the amount of impurities present in the clay; lime, alkalies such as magnesia, soda and potash, all lowering the fusion point considerably.

Colour of the finished brick is related to the amount of iron impurities present in the clay; when the amount of ferric oxide is greater than 4 or 5 per cent., the brick will burn to a good red colour; above 8 per cent. of iron oxides will form a blue burnt brick; less than 3 per cent. will produce a buff or whitish brick.

When a clay is being considered for brick-making, the above different qualities will be secured according to the purpose for which the brick is wanted, by mixing a suitable clay base. A fat clay can be rendered lean by the admixture of sand or ' grog '. Grog is burnt clay powdered, or ground-up brick debris. The plasticity of a clay can be reduced by adding alkalies, but this will lower the fusion point, and will be safe only with a brick that is to be burned at a low temperature. The colour can be influenced by modifying the content of iron oxides. As a rough working indication, a brick clay should contain approximately three-fifths of its bulk of silica, one-fifth of alumina, the other fifth being made up of the total of iron oxides, lime and alkalies, etc.

Clays that can be used for brick-making occur at a great many geological horizons, but the older clays have been altered by pressure to shale, which at first sight has none of the properties of clay. Wherever the material is secured in the raw state—whether as shale, or partially indurated clay, or rough clay from a fairly recent source—it is first softened and broken small by weathering. Many brick shales are quarried and laid out on the ground to be broken down by frost and rain for a long period before use. The material is ground up and incorporated with water sufficient to make it plastic in a pug-mill. By analysis and trial, the deficiency or excess of certain ingredients will have been determined, and addition of other materials—sand or clay of other qualities—is made to correct these factors. The greatest care must be taken to secure homogeneity of all the materials; all must be reduced to the finest particles and completely mixed, for if lumps of one ingredient are left, flaws will result in the baking and cooling.

Of the more widely used brick-making materials, true clays are obtained from the Lias, Gault and London Clay; the shales of the Coal Measures and Millstone Grits provide a large amount of material that has to be weathered and ground before use; the glacial clays over the whole country are used, but always need the most careful grading, as by their very nature they are a mixed and rapidly variable deposit, changing almost foot by foot in any exposure. Some very fine brick clays and ' brick earths ' (lean, earthy or sandy clays) are obtained from the deposits of silt and clay that have filled up ancient glacial lakes. These often have great uniformity of character over a wide area, and lend thmselves to the making of special-quality bricks.

Pottery Clays.

A clay which has considerable plasticity, and at the same time can be so treated as to maintain a correct shape while burning, will be used for pottery. It is desirable that such a clay burns white or cream (' biscuit ') and bakes hard and of extremely fine texture. It must be free from shrinkage cracks and warping on cooling. The finest of all pottery clays is kaolin, or ' china clay ', which is used for the finest porcelain manufacture. This is derived from the weathering of felspars, as explained in Chapter II. A clay that contains a high percentage of true kaolin and is free from deleterious impurities will be used for pottery and, if it has slight local characteristics, will give rise to a local type of product distinguishable from any other. The Poole pottery is produced from a particular clay occurring in the Bagshot series of strata, of Eocene age. The Trias clays of Watcombe and the Bovey Tracey Beds of South Devon (the latter of Oligocene age) are both used extensively for special pottery.

In all cases the pottery clays need the most careful washing and grading of materials and constant check on their composition and physical properties. Earthenwares and sanitary white ware are made from selected Coal Measure clays (shales).

Refractories.

The refractories include refractory clays and also several pure rock types. The commonest refractory clay is ' fireclay '. This is mainly found as the underclay or seat-earth on which a coal-seam rests, and is actually the ancient soil of the forest, the remains of which have made the coal. From its long support of abundant plant life, all the potash and soda compounds and all salts that can be used by plants have been extracted, and little remains of iron and other mineral salts. The composition varies from aluminous clay to ganister, which is almost pure silica. The best fireclays are soft greyish clays of moderate plasticity, which crumble more or less readily when weathered. The underclays are very rarely bedded, being usually a nearly homogeneous layer from a few inches to a few feet thick, immediately underlying the coal. The fireclay is tested in various ways; chemical analysis will give the alkali and impurity content, which should be very low indeed; a heating test is applied to estimate the refractoriness, and it is necessary also to test the resistance to corrosion by slags, abrasion, etc., as most fireclays are used to make bricks or materials for furnace linings. The silica content will vary between about 55 per cent. and 75 per cent. There are many so-called ' bastard fireclays ' which contain sufficient alkalies to lower their refractoriness below the limits for firebrick use, and these are generally used for salt glaze and sanitary ware, building-bricks, coarse pottery and ' stoneware '. When baked, they form a vitrified impervious ware, which has no tendency to twist and warp, such as would be present in clays of lower fusibility point. The whole of the fireclays come from the Coal Measures, mainly from the Middle and Upper series, of the productive coal-fields.

Closely allied to fireclay is the rock ganister. The grains making up ganister are seen under the microscope to be very angular, and such cement as is present is itself pure silica. A good ganister varies in composition between 89 per cent. and 99 per cent. silica. It is used as a raw material for making silica bricks for furnace linings, for moulding sand for certain types of steel castings and, made into a ' compo ' with about 5 per cent. of ground fireclay, as a clay for lining and luting furnaces. To make silica bricks, the ganister is ground up, mixed with a small proportion of milk of lime, and burned at a temperature between 1200° C. and 1500° C. These bricks are both strong enough and infusible enough to be used for the lining of acid hearth steel furnaces.

Magnesian limestone from the Permian formation can be burned to produce magnesia, which is a valuable refractory, and used for furnace linings. This has a marked basic chemical reaction with molten metal, and is therefore limited in its use to basic hearth processes. For exceptionally strong refractory bricks, chromite is occasionally used, but none occurs in this country.

Lime and Cements.

Much lime is burned and used for the production of builder's mortar, this being a mixture of lime and sand or fine ashes, ground and mixed together. For this ordinary quicklime is used, slaked by the addition of water, then mixed with the other ingredient. Some mortars are 'rendered' with a little cement or other constituent to help the setting, or to prevent the crumbling that often follows the setting of a pure lime–sand mortar.

Cements are principally of two types: 'Portland' and 'hydraulic'. A Portland cement consists of a finely ground mixture of lime, silica and alumina, which will set rapidly to form stable compounds with water. In the Lower Carboniferous rocks of Northumberland and South Scotland there is a great thickness of strata of alternating limestones and shales with some sandstones, the limestones of which are called 'cement-stones' and give this name to the whole series. These cement-stones are very impure limestones, with nearly half and half composition lime and clay. When burned together and finely ground they produce a natural cement of Portland type. The mixture of lime and clay is roasted in a kiln, and the temperature and other conditions control the nature of the product.

Portland cement is made from a mixture of calcareous materials, which may be in the form of chalk, limestone, shells, calcareous mud, etc., and clay, which again may be in many forms, clay, shale, slate, etc., and a small quantity of slag or other siliceous material. The ingredients are finely ground and conveyed to a kiln, where they are heated to a temperature at which they form clinkers. The clinkers are cooled and ground to form the cement. The approximate composition has wide limits, lime between 55 per cent. and 70 per cent., alumina 4–12 per cent., magnesia and iron to about 5 per cent., and the rest silica. Much cement has been made from chalk ballast and the dredged mud from the Medway, but recently large cement works have opened out on the Carboniferous Limestone.

A second group is that of the rapidly hardening cements, which have the same ingredients as Portland cement, but in different proportions. The alumina and lime are both present about 35 per cent., with about 6–10 per cent. of silica, and some compounds of iron. This material after grinding is heated in the kiln until it clinkers, then raised to a higher temperature, at which the clinker fuses. This fused mass is then ground extremely fine: On mixing with water and sand or gravel to make a concrete, it sets very rapidly, and so avoids the danger of frost damage, that can be so serious with Portland cement.

Hydraulic lime or cement has the property of setting under water, and so is of the greatest importance in dock and harbour work, water-works construction, etc. It is prepared from limestone nodules that occur in several shale formations of different geological ages. The best known are the ' Blue Lias Limestones ', nodular limestones with a composition approximately 60 per cent. carbonate of lime, 34 per cent. clay and 4 per cent. or more of iron. The cement stones are burned in conical kilns, usually coke-fired. It is not burned so fiercely as for Portland cement. When finely ground it is ready for use, but cannot safely be stored for a long period, as it is liable to deteriorate rapidly on exposure to air. It has nothing like the strength of Portland cement.

Plaster of Paris and Parian cements are prepared from the mineral gypsum, by baking the gypsum in specially designed ovens to get rid of the water of crystallisation. On baking, it falls to a soft white powder which, when mixed to a paste with water, is plastic for a short while, soon setting hard with considerable strength and solidity. Stucco is made by mixing it with glue instead of water. Parian cement and Keene's cement are prepared from plaster of Paris by mixing the burned gypsum with a saturated solution of alum, borax or sulphate of potash. After soaking it is taken out and baked again, ground to powder, then moistened with a solution of alum It forms a very hard plaster, which will take a high polish. Keene's cement is made with alum, and Parian with borax. There are extensive beds of gypsum in the base of the Triassic system and in parts of the upper Permian in this country, and large plaster industries are settled on them in the Vale of Eden (Cumberland), around Hartlepool and other parts of South Durham, and in Cheshire, where these formations have their maximum development.

CHAPTER XIV

Mining geology: Mineral veins; placer deposits—gold, platinum, tin; gold reef deposits of Africa; segregation deposits—nickel, iron, etc. Bedded ores: iron ores of Britain; bauxite and laterite; magnesite. Chemical deposits—gypsum and anhydrite, salt and potash.

GEOLOGY and mining are so closely allied as to overlap on many subjects and to share many investigations in common. Both are concerned with the occurrence within the crust of the earth of deposits of minerals, the geologist being mainly interested in the origin and significance in earth history of the minerals, and the miner in the possibility and methods of getting the minerals out of the deposits in useable form. Both need to understand the shape of deposits and the habits and associations of the minerals one with another, and this forms their common ground.

Economic minerals (those used as the raw materials of the metallurgical and other industries) fall naturally into two principal groups, according to their mode of origin—the vein minerals, which occupy more or less vertical fissures cutting across the strata, and the bedded minerals, which occur among the strata, being themselves special types of deposit, formed during the deposition of the normal strata. There are a few intermediate groups that will need only brief mention.

The vein minerals are always associated with large intrusions of igneous rocks, in the majority of cases with batholiths of acid rock. When such batholiths are intruded, the overlying strata are arched up and tension cracks are formed on the crest and flanks of the arch. These form the channels for the deposition of vein minerals. All acid rock magmas contain a small percentage of metallic elements and compounds, mostly in solution in free silica. Along with them are small traces of elements such as fluorine and sulphur, which are extremely volatile.

When the mass of magma begins to cool, the constituent minerals crystallise out in the order of their melting points, from the highest to the lowest. When the felspars, micas and much of the quartz have solidified, there is considerable contraction with the cooling of the whole mass and some amount of squeezing by the growth of the crystals, which squeezes out from the crystal 'sponge' the remaining liquid residuum. This consists of silica with fluorine, and many metals and metallic compounds, which have lower melting points than the rock-forming mineral silicates. This liquor, with its heavy content of most of the metallic elements that were present in the magma, is forced up the tension cracks and small faults towards the surface of the ground. As the liquor passes upward it moves steadily into areas of lower temperature, and is itself progressively cooled. In this progress the minerals that are in solution in the silica crystallise out as their melting (or freezing) point is reached, crystallising on to the sides of the vein fissure. As the whole temperature falls, other minerals of possibly lower freezing point crystallise as a second layer over the ones first formed, and finally the whole fissure may be filled solid with the last silica or fluoride liquor. Thus we get a vein structure that varies in content as it gets farther from the original intrusion and that has a layered structure at most parts, with bands of mineral more or less symmetrically placed on the two walls, with layers of different minerals in succession towards the centre.

The non-metallic minerals filling up the vein, and in which many of the metallic ores are enclosed, are called the gangue minerals, and these also vary with the temperature zones. The compounds that the metals form are rather varied. In the deeper zones, tungsten and arsenic will combine with other metals to form tungstates and arsenides. In the zones nearest the surface there is a great deal of 'secondary' alteration of minerals, brought about by percolating waters charged with oxygen and lime in solution. These waters react chemically with the minerals and produce oxides and carbonates in the so-called zone of oxidation. These various zones are best set out in the form of a table (after

Dewey), with the appropriate gangue minerals, and the approximate temperature at which they are formed.

Gangue minerals.	Mineral zones.	Approx. temperature of formation, ° C.
quartz → tourmaline → fluorspar → arsenic → barytes → sulphides → tungstates → calcite →	Zones of carbonates of iron, manganese, etc., sulphides of antimony.	Up to 150
	Zone of sulphides of lead and silver, sometimes carbonated when near the surface. In depth these give place to zinc and lead, then to zinc and copper sulphides.	400
	Zone of sulphides of copper mixed with tin and tungsten near the base of the zone.	
	Zone of oxide of tin, with wolfram (tungstate of iron and manganese) in the upper part.	550 to 575

It will be noticed that barytes appears in the list of gangue minerals, although it is a metallic mineral—sulphate of barium. It is the invariable habit of both barytes and the carbonate of barium, witherite, to act and occur as gangue minerals, often forming a matrix in which much of the lead ore is carried.

This zoning of the minerals is seen fairly clearly in the different areas of this country. In Cornwall, where erosion has removed the upper strata and revealed the tops of the granite intrusions, the veins in the uppermost parts of the granite and in the country rock close to the granite contact produce ores of tin and tungsten. As the veins are worked farther away from the granite, and thus in a colder zone at the time of formation, the principal ores are those of copper, with some lead and zinc still farther from the granites. In the Lake District the mineral veins near the Skiddaw Granite, and between it and Carrock Fell, produce tungsten and its occasional associate, molybdenum, with copper ores farther away, and in strata that are con-considerably higher than those in which the tungsten occurs there are great quantities of copper, zinc and lead obtained. This evidently belongs to the second zone, and passes upward into the base of the lead–silver zone. In the Pennines and in North Wales the lead-mining fields of the Carboniferous Limestone areas are working in the lead–silver zone and the underlying igneous mass from which the veins originate is nowhere seen and can only be inferred from the distribution of the mineralisation. Where the veins traverse a series of limestones it is found that silica has frequently reacted with the limestone, producing 'silicified' beds adjacent to the vein, the silica replacing the calcium carbonate of the limestone, and the carbonate often reacting with the vein solutions, making calcite the commonest gangue material. It is in such areas that barytes also becomes a common gangue mineral.

In some of the areas where the veins traverse thick limestones the vein solutions have reacted with the lime-stone of a particular bed for some distance on each side of the vein, and silica and minerals have replaced large portions of it. Such altered limestones form 'flats' where the ores are found impregnating the limestone, sometimes in workable proportions. In the Alston Moor and Weardale districts flatting of this kind is fairly common. In Rodderhope Fell the Tynebottom limestone is impregnated with silica and with ores of zinc and lead, for a considerable distance on each side of one of the principal veins, and forms a deposit of great economic value (Fig. 20).

In all vein and flat deposits the vein filling and country rock have to be taken out to the width necessary for working, and the mixture of rock, gangues and ores (called 'bouse') is crushed to a fine sand and then washed. Most of the washing consists of using running streams or currents of water of sufficient velocity to float or wash off the lighter rock and gangue minerals and leave behind the much heavier ores. Further washing and treatment will separate the ores of different kinds and the heavy gangues such as barytes. The ores so separated are then ready for the smelter, who by varied heat treatment obtains the pure metal from them.

Veins are usually found to be small faults of little throw, and, like faults, they incline a little from the vertical, run for long distances across country, and frequently branch into ' strings '—smaller and narrower fault fissures.

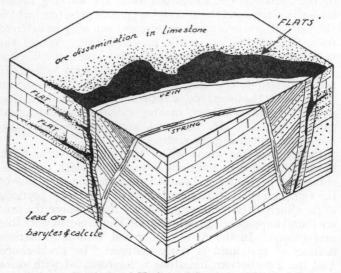

FIG. 20.—Vertical and Horizontal Sections of Mineral Vein and Flats.

The width of vein fissure is closely related to the strata through which it is passing, so that a vein traversing limestone or sandstone can often stand as a fairly wide open fissure and contain good metal; while passing through shales, the fissure is closed up with broken shale and clay, and rarely bears well. It is in this that the geological knowledge of the strata of an area can be of considerable importance to the prospector looking for the possibilities of mineral veins.

Placer Deposits.

Where streams have eroded a piece of country that is crossed by mineral veins there is every prospect of finding placer deposits, provided erosion has not gone too far. The gravel and sand eroded by the stream from the exposed rocks will contain fragments of minerals derived from the veins and the process of washing and shifting the gravels by the stream water will be almost the same in effect as the washing that a miner gives to the bouse to separate the ore from the waste. In any pools or fine gravel banks, where the stream velocity changes, fragments of ore or metal will be dropped by a current that can still remove the rock, and so in such places there will be gradual accumulation of mineral sand. This is the commonest form of occurrence of gold deposits. The gold occurs in quartz veins, as the native metal, and is usually present in small specks and ' dust ' with occasional larger lumps—the ' nuggets '. When the quartz vein is eroded by a stream, the quartz soon shatters and the gold dust is released. By its great density and its complete freedom from attack by water or chemical impurities, it accumulates in the sands and gravels, and with washing and re-washing, soon forms a fairly rich natural concentration or ' streak ' in the bottom of the gravel banks and pools. The gold-miner seeks out such likely places, and by ' panning ' the gravel—that is, giving it an artificial re-wash—he can soon detect the presence of gold grains. The mining then proceeds by open quarrying of the gravel and putting it through simple washers. When the gravels are very thick, small shafts are sunk to reach the bottom layers in which is the greatest concentration of gold. In modern mining, the gravels are sometimes treated by mechanical dredgers or by hydraulic sluicing, but in all methods the principles involved are the same. Small quantities of gold have been got from placer deposits in the Leadhills area of South Scotland, and in parts of Ireland, particularly the Wicklow mountains. There are a few quartz veins which are gold bearing in North Wales and also in Ireland, and some of these and the placers have been worked since before the Roman era.

In Cornwall most of the early mining of tin was confined to placer deposits, all the streams which cross the granite areas having large quantities of ' stream tin ' in their beds. In recent times some tin has even been recovered from deposits washed out to sea by the Cornish rivers. Much of the tin ore of the Malayan peninsula is in placer form. Platinum is another very heavy metal that occurs as placer deposits. Lead and zinc may occur in this way, but their ores are too brittle to remain in visible size, and after only a moderate washing they are reduced to too fine a powder to be recoverable.

The great gold-mining areas of the Rand in South Africa are in fact working on an ancient placer deposit. The gold there occurs in the quartz matrix of a peculiar rock called ' banket '. This is an ancient conglomerate of river pebbles, themselves nearly all of quartz, cemented together by silica. This deposit is geologically very old and has been folded into a deep syncline and covered by many later strata. The material of the banket is in fact a true placer gravel, with the gold concentrate now included in the silica matrix. The whole rock is mined, and since the structure of the banket in its deep syncline was known, some of the deepest shafts in the world have been sunk to the trough of the fold. The whole banket is brought out and ground up to powder, then the gold is extracted chemically by the solvent action of cyanide, and later recovered from the cyanide and purified by furnace refining. The edges of the syncline outcrop as long ' reefs ' along which the gold was first discovered.

Much of the gold of Alaska and California is in placer deposits and some of the gold of Australia, but the most important sources in India are in veins. The abundant gold resources of Siberia are again mainly in placer deposits. If the erosion has not proceeded too far, there is always a chance that the veins from which placers are derived might be discovered, and a prospector finding placer gravels will follow up the stream to examine all the country to its source, in the hope of striking the original reef or vein complex.

Diamonds sometimes occur as placer deposits, but their distribution is very limited indeed, all being related to the peculiar diamond ' pipes ' of Kimberley and that part of Africa. These are very ancient igneous intrusions, in form like the neck of an ancient volcano. They are circular in plan, and extend vertically down into the earth for great distances, no bottom having yet been reached. The ' pipe ' is filled with badly weathered and altered, ultra-basic rock, and in this ' blue ground ' the diamonds occur very sparingly. In the area where pipes occur the older river gravels formed during the erosion of the pipes contain a few placer diamonds.

Segregation Ores.

Closely related to the diamond deposits are occurrences of ore by so-called ' segregation ' within a large igneous mass. The greatest example of this type is found in the nickel deposits of Sudbury, Ontario, from which the bulk of all the world's nickel is obtained. The ores occur in a large mass of basic igneous rock that forms a laccolith. During the cooling of the injected magma there was time for some of the heavier constituents to sink through the liquid and concentrate near the base of the mass. This bottom portion, a natural gravity separation, contains both nickel ores, some small but valuable proportion of platinum, and many sulphide ores. The whole mass of this bottom layer of the rock is quarried and mined, crushed and treated in many ways for the separation and recovery of the various metals. Small deposits of nickel ores at Petsamo in Finland are of the same type, occurring as segregations in basic rocks. Many of the first-quality iron ores of Sweden are segregations in large igneous intrusions, and are usually in the form of titaniferous iron ore, or ilmenite. The famous iron mines of Dannemora in Sweden are in a segregation of magnetite (iron ore) in an intrusion of diorite. Most of the segregation ores are those of iron and chromium, both occurring as the oxides, and iron, nickel and copper, occurring in the sulphide form.

Bedded Ores.

There are a large number of important metalliferous deposits, which owe their origin to chemical action taking place at a definite stage intermittent between normal sedimentary deposition, and resulting in ores that lie as a definite bed or stratum between other conformable strata. The most important of these are the bedded iron ores.

These bedded ores have been formed by ordinary processes of sedimentation in waters that were rich in iron in solution. The iron may have been precipitated by chemical action or by the action of a group of iron-depositing bacteria. The conditions under which they can form are probably similar to those found in many lagoons to-day—a large and shallow area of sea cut off from the full force of ocean currents and storms, where sedimentation can go on very slowly and quietly. The muds which accumulate on the floor of the lagoon are rich in compounds of iron.

There are two main groups of iron-bearing sediments in this country: the ironstones of the Coal Measures, and the bedded ores of the Lias and Inferior Oolite (Lower Jurassic). The clay ironstones of the Coal Measures are found in the shales above certain coal seams, and consist of ovate nodules containing about 30 per cent. iron in the form of carbonate, with the rest of the bulk made up of clay and calcite with some organic coaly material. Above some seams there are continuous thin beds of 'black-band' ironstone, which is similar to the clay ironstone, except that it has more coaly constituents. The clay ironstones need the addition of some fuel to calcine them before smelting, but the black-band ores have sufficient organic material to calcine themselves if they are once fired. It was these bedded ironstones that were used for many centuries as the main source of iron in this country, but now, except for parts of Staffordshire and Scotland, they are little used. To amateur geologists the nodules are of interest, as they seem generally to form in the mud of the swamp or lagoon, around some small fragment of organic material, a portion of a plant, an insect, or a few fish-scales, and in them, if properly split, are found some of the best fossils to be obtained from the series.

The bedded ores of the Lias and Lower Jurassic series form actual continuous beds, sometimes up to 20 feet or more thick. These are oolitic, and most of the ooliths (small spherical concretions) are made of silicates and carbonates of iron. The iron content of the bed is again rather low, not more than about 30 per cent. at the most, and the organic matter that is present contains a fair proportion of phosphorus and sulphur. Until recent times it was almost impossible to smelt these ores successfully, as they could not be used for the Bessemer process of steel-making, where phosphorus and sulphur will spoil the quality at once. It was not until the basic-hearth process of steel-making, with better methods of smelting for pig iron, were introduced, that these ores became important. They are now responsible for about 80 per cent. of all the British production of iron, and in the Lorraine ironfields of France constitute the largest iron resources in Europe.

The beds of ironstone occur at several horizons in the Lias, both in the Lower, Middle and Upper series, and in each case there are usually more than one bed. In the Cleveland district of Yorkshire, the following is an average section.

Inferior Oolite.	*Top seam ironstone.*	4 to 9 feet.
Upper Lias.	Shale.	260 feet.
	Main seam ironstone.	5 to 12 feet.
	Shale.	6 feet.
	Pecten seam ironstone.	1½ to 6 feet.
Middle Lias.	Shale.	6 feet.
	Two-foot seam ironstone.	2 feet.
	Shale.	20 to 30 feet.
	Avicula seam ironstone.	3 feet.

The ironstones of the Inferior Oolite are the basis of the iron industry around Kettering and in Northampton and Rutland, and the Lias ironstones in the newly developed iron-mining areas of Oxford, Leicester and Lincolnshire. At the most extensive new works at Corby, the ironstones lie under a moderate cover of soft rocks, at a depth which allows of working by mechanical navvy. The great steam crane navvies lift off the overlying rock and soil along a trench more than a mile long, dumping it regularly behind them, and then take out the ironstone below. The ground is thus remade behind the excavators as they move forward steadily along this mile-long front.

There are important deposits of bedded iron ores similar in character but of greater geological age in Newfoundland and in the United States, in New York State and extending to Alabama, a distance of about 1200 miles.

Replacement Ores.

The iron ores of Cumberland and Furness (North Lanca-shire) are of a type generally described as replacement, or metosomatic ores. The ore is principally hæmatite (an oxide of iron), and is found in enormous masses, replacing the Carboniferous Limestone in the region of some of the larger faults that cut through the overlying Permian and Trias, and through the limestones. The sandstones which are the main part of the Permian and Trias systems in this area are desert sands, with polished rounded grains, and all the grains have a pellicle or thin skin of iron oxide, giving the sandstone the bright red colour that has given it the name New Red Sandstone. In the region of the faults there is some evidence of bleaching of the colour, and it seems clear that percolating waters through many geo-logical periods have passed through the New Red Sandstone, taking out some of the iron in solution, and then passing deeper down the fault fissures. These iron-charged waters have reacted chemically with the limestone and the calcite has been dissolved away particle by particle and iron oxide deposited in its place. This is seen both by the relation of the iron-ore bodies to faults and by the fact that where thin beds of shale traverse the limestone, they are not altered to ironstone, but remain as shale. Also fossils preserved in calcite in the limestone are changed to hæmatite. The reaction is thus seen to be limited to the calcite of the limestone.

Iron ores of similar origin are found in the Forest of Dean, but there the principal ore is brown oxide of iron, not hæmatite. The ore-field of Bilbao, North Spain, is also an area where the hæmatite ores are replacement bodies in limestone.

Replacement of calcareous rocks by other ores occasionally takes place, but none of them to the same extent as the iron ores. Near the lead veins in the limestones of this country there are patches where the lead ore has replaced limestone, evidenced by the rare occurrence of a fossil completely preserved in galena (lead sulphide). The replacement that has occurred near veins is slightly different from that discussed in the case of iron, as the former takes place at the high temperature of vein formation, while the iron replacement is made at the ordinary ground temperature. The replacement hæmatites are valuable ores specially suitable for use in the Bessemer steel-making process because of their extremely low content of phosphorus and sulphur.

There are certain deposits that are the source of important metals, iron, aluminium, and magnesium, which cannot be classed as true ores, but which have the economic importance of ore bodies. In the earlier account of the weathering of igneous rocks (Chapter II, p. 20) it was shown how an igneous rock on decomposition by weathering agents may produce from some of the silicate minerals, clays of various composition. Clay is mainly hydrated aluminium silicates, with more or less admixture of iron oxides as impurity. When conditions are such that an aluminous clay is produced in which the dominant constituents are aluminium oxides in hydrated form, with only small amounts of silica and iron oxides, this clay is called **bauxite**, and can be smelted for the production of metallic aluminium. Although aluminium is actually the most abundant metal in the accessible parts of the earth's crust, there are very few forms in which it occurs that can be smelted, and of these only bauxite is at all common. The clay takes its name from Les Baux in Southern France, where it may be an ancient deposit from hot springs. In most cases it is derived directly from igneous rocks—in Northern Ireland it is associated with the Antrim basalts, in Scotland with igneous rocks. Its composition generally ranges around 60–65 per cent. aluminium oxide, and iron oxides about 6 per cent. The bauxites may be found where they originated, as a covering to decayed beds of the igneous rock from which they are derived, or they may have been transported by streams and re-deposited.

When the decay of the igneous rocks, particularly the more basic ones, is such that large quantities of iron oxides are left along with the alumina, the mineral is called laterite, and is regarded as a low-grade iron ore. True laterite is chiefly developed under tropical conditions of weathering, but there is every possible gradation and intermixture of the two types, bauxite and laterite.

True laterite covers many large areas of igneous rocks in the tropics, the Deccan Plateau of India, the Malay Peninsula, Dutch East Indies, great parts of Africa, South America and Western Australia. Its composition depends largely on the composition of the rock from which it is derived, and also on its subsequent history. Like bauxite, there are two kinds of laterite deposits: those which are in place on the rocks from which they derive, and those which have been transported and re-deposited. All laterites have in common the scarcity of silica, magnesia and alkalies, but may contain large proportions of manganese. In India there are vast deposits of manganiferous laterites which are worked as a source of manganese.

Another residual mineral produced by the decay of basic igneous rocks is magnesite, the carbonate of magnesium. It is mainly used, not for production of the metal, but as a basic refractory material used in many metallurgical operations. It occurs like bauxite, both associated with the parent rock and also in considerable re-deposited masses. Its chief occurrence is in Eastern Europe, in Austria, Greece and the Grecian Archipelago. As it occurs like any other sedimentary deposit, its outcrops have been mapped across country, and places have been selected for working it where it outcrops on steeply rising ground and where it can be got in large-scale open quarrying. There are other sources of it in Canada and the United States, but it is rare in the rest of the world.

Chemical Deposits.

These consist of beds of more or less pure salts, which have been precipitated during the course of deposition of normal strata and which lie like more or less persistent normal strata within the general sequence. The principal products are gypsum and anhydrite (sulphates of calcium), rocksalt (sodium chloride), potash and soda salts, phosphates and celestine (strontium sulphate).

There are two ways in which such deposits originate; by far the commonest is by drying up of an enclosed area of sea-water, with the crystallisation of the different salts contained in it, in the inverse order of their solubility, the least soluble being precipitated first and the most soluble last; in some conditions, where such an enclosed sea is receiving fine mud or wind-blown detritus at the same time, marls or fine muds will be formed, in which the salts will be incorporated. In this latter case the salt may be found as isolated crystals dispersed throughout the formation. The second group are derived by denudation from masses of igneous rock which are weathering. China clay and bauxite are examples of this, the prime condition necessary being the facility for the denudation products to accumulate reasonably free from other detritus so that an economically valuable deposit may be formed.

During the later part of the Permian and the greater part of Triassic periods in Europe there was a condition of aridity of climate which produced deserts of wide extent. The remnants of the Carboniferous sea that remained in Europe enclosed by new mountain chains, were then progressively dried up, and during that evaporation most of our chemical deposits were formed. The magnesian limestone (calcium-magnesium carbonate) was the earliest precipitate, followed by gypsum in intermittent beds, so that the gypsum occurs as numerous beds separated by the limestone. As drying up continued the limestone gradually ceased and the gypsum accompanied by an-hydrite (calcium sulphate) continued to be deposited. This is followed in turn by rocksalt, and the potash salts in various mixtures, last of all. The work of the geologist is to study the containing rock system, and from its geology determine the former full extent of these desert seas. The earliest substances to be precipitated will extend over the whole former extent of the sea, but successive salts will be deposited in shrinking areas, and the last, potash salts, will occur only near the last remnants, the deeper pools of the lake. From the study of sedimentation and strati-graphy the extent of the lakes at the various stages has been worked out, and then borings are put down at selected points to test the presence or absence and thickness of salts. The main basins are around South Durham, where near Middlesbrough there are beds of gypsum, anhydrite and rocksalt; in Cheshire there are extensive beds of rocksalt, while the bulk of the potash salts lie in North Germany and in Alsace, though the Alsace deposits are thought to be of Oligocene age.

Celestine occurs in this country only in the Keuper Marls near Bristol. These are thin bedded marly deposits of Triassic age, and probably represent extremely fine silt and wind-blown dust, carried into a local lake or pool of limited extent. Strontium salts were present in the water, possibly brought in from the weathering of some local rock not now known. The mineral has crystallised in the marl while it was still soft mud, and is now obtained by quarrying and breaking up the marl and picking out the large crystals, often several inches in length.

The phosphate minerals so important as fertilisers are mainly derived from altered limestones which have been attacked by phosphate-rich water. In most cases the source of the phosphate is originally found in deposits of guano or of coprolites (bird and animal excrement), which, when they rest upon or near limestone or coral rock, are leached by percolating water, which then reacts chemically with the calcium carbonate, producing phosphate of lime. These products are thus of hybrid nature; partly original deposits, partly replacement. There are some ancient deposits of phosphatic limestone of Permian age in Idaho, and of Ordovician age in Arkansas and other of the United States. Large bedded phosphate deposits are found in Northern Africa, mainly in Tunis, of Eocene age.

CHAPTER XV

Fuel minerals—coal—problems of coal-mining. Oil—geological prospecting for oil. Some modern methods of prospecting.

Coal.

THE formation of coal has been described briefly in Chapter II, and the conditions in the Coal Measure swamps in Chapter IX. It is only necessary to add a little about the actual changes that take place, by which forest trees and plants become in the course of time a coal seam. In the swamp conditions the trees, which, unlike most of our present trees, had a very strong outer bark layer and a pithy, soft middle, had little strength and were easily overthrown as they grew old. The fallen trunks along with the remains of the abundant undergrowth formed deep beds of water-logged peaty leaf-mould, which on their decay produced weak organic acids, ulmic and humic. These have the properties of a preservative of vegetable tissue, so that the water-covered plant matter was saved from further decay, but gradually softened down to a pulpy mass, very like peat. The forests were frequently interrupted by long periods of subsidence, during which muds and sands were swept over their site by the rivers or seas, completely burying the peat and sealing it off from the air. Under these conditions the peat gradually loses some of its oxygen, so that its proportion of carbon rises rapidly in comparison with its other constituents. In a mature peat, which is well compacted and has been buried for a few centuries or more, the percentage of carbon will be about 50–60 per cent. with 30 or 40 per cent. of oxygen. With the continued cover and rapidly increased pressure that result from the burying under later strata, more of the oxygen is lost, and the carbon increase is marked by increasing hardness of the material, until a stage is reached where the stuff has a stony hardness and character, and becomes coal. The coals of many kinds are classified in a continuous series by their proportions of carbon, oxygen and hydrogen content. The whole group is spoken of as the 'coal series', and the approximate compositions are as follows.

Name.	Carbon, %.	Oxygen, %.	Hydrogen, %.
PEAT	50–65	30–40	5–7
LIGNITE . . .	65–70	20–30	6–7
Sub-BITUMINOUS COAL.	70–78	13–20	7–8
BITUMINOUS COAL .	78–85	6–13	7–9
Anthracites . . .	85–95	2–6	3–6

The Lignite is often called Brown Coal, and still retains a little of its woody texture, and is very light. The sub-bituminous and bituminous coals are soft and smoky house-coals and the softer steam coals, while anthracite is a hard coal, needing special draught to burn properly, and is mainly reserved for naval use.

The problem in coal-mining that is most often placed before the geologist is that of 'correlation'—the task of identifying particular seams in two or three different places, often many miles apart, and naming them correctly. A variant of this is to determine, from the strata that have been exposed by boring or sinking a shaft, just what position in the Coal Measures has been reached in relation to well-known workable coal-seams. In the mine the commonest form of the problem is met when a fault has been encountered. In the narrow limits of a mine gallery it is very difficult, if not impossible, to tell which is the hade of the fault, and the problem arises at once, has the coal-seam in which the gallery was driven been shifted up or down? will the miner have to put up a small shaft, or sink one, to continue working in the same seam, and also, how far will he have to rise or sink? Within an area of a few square miles, the general method is to rely on an accurately recorded 'shaft section'. When the shaft of a colliery is being sunk, every individual layer of rock, even to the thickness of only an inch or so, is carefully measured and recorded with all its characters, colour, jointing, fossils and anything whatever that will enable one to recognise it again. The changes in the strata of the Coal Measures are so rapid, and sandstones, shales, thin coals, etc., alternate so frequently that it is almost impossible to have an identical succession repeated in the whole vertical thickness. On passing through the fault, the miner or geologist will make an excavation in roof or floor, sufficient to get a succession of two or three layers, or to find, if he is lucky, a distinctive layer; then, having examined and measured them, he will carefully study the shaft section and note the position of the corresponding strata. The miners become very skilled in this, soon learning to recognise with certainty the strata immediately above and below the seam they are working. To enable similar comparisons to be made over a wide area, the Institute of Mining Engineers and the Geological Survey have collected and published large volumes of 'sections of strata', in which all the measured borehole and shaft sections are recorded in detail, for most coal-fields.

The geologist can add to this method of correlation others that depend on a study of the fossils found in the strata and in the coal itself. Most coal-seams have, immediately above them, a series of fine blackish or grey shales that mark the overwhelming of the forest by mud and which are the result of the first stage of subsidence. In many cases these shales accumulated while the area was a large lake or lagoon in which fresh-water 'mussels' flourished. The remains of these shells fill the shale in particular bands, and the interval of time between one seam and the next is often long enough for considerable changes to have taken place in either the form or the proportions in which different forms are present. In all the Coal Measures there are a number of these 'mussel bands' which are recognisable over very wide areas, often from one coal-field to another. Their position in relation to the best-known seams is also known, so that a shaft-sinking which reaches a particular mussel bed can be said with a large measure of certainty to be so many feet above a particular seam. In some cases, where collieries have nearly worked out a seam, it has been thought that that was the lowest valuable seam in the area, but a study of the mussel bands has proved that older miners have confused the names and the seam is actually not the lowest. A deepening of the shaft has then brought still further seams into production.

A similar correlation can now be made from the microscopic fossils contained in the coal itself. The spores which make up so much of the dull coal have been mentioned, and in some cases these, or the proportions in which they are present, are characteristic of a particular seam. A separation of spores from the coal can be examined, or the larger ones can be seen in a micro-section of the coal, and in many cases the actual seam being examined can be named with certainty.

The study of the nature and extent of the folding that has affected coal-fields since their deposition has enabled many concealed areas of coal-bearing strata to be predicted, in deep down-folds since covered by later rocks. In this country and on the Continent several coal areas have been discovered by this line of reasoning, and then proved by borings, and later brought into production. The Kent coal-field and the Dutch coal-field are examples of this.

The geological knowledge of the structure of a coal-field has great bearing on problems of drainage and the location of the most advantageous pumping stations, shafts, etc. In many minor ways the knowledge of geology is of value to the miner, and in fact most miners are by practice and experience good geologists in their own particular strata.

Oil.

The origin of deposits of oil is still a matter for much discussion, but is largely dependent on the evidence of chemists as well as geologists. The prime geological factor in oil-mining is the conditions under which oil products are concentrated into very localised areas, so as to be sufficiently abundant for exploitation. Oily and bituminous substances are present in many rocks in dispersed small quantities; in the darker Carboniferous lime-stones there are sufficient bitumens to give the rock a powerful smell when freshly broken.

Whatever may be the exact origin of oil, it occurs most commonly in the incoherent sands and silts of Tertiary age, and is dependent on particular geological conditions for its concentration. In many of these rocks the oil is mixed with ground-water, but if the strata are folded up into a sharp anticline, the oil and water separate under gravity, the oil floating on top of the water and being brought by the steep flanks of the anticline into the very peak or crest of the fold. It is necessary for the formation of an ' oil pool ' that the pervious sandy strata is covered by impervious clays or shales, to prevent the general diffusion of the oil away from the flanks of the fold. When the crest of the fold reaches the surface or is reached by tension cracks from the surface, the oil may seep out at ground level and form a ' seepage '. In many ancient seepages the more volatile part of the oil has long ago disappeared, and left only the thicker, tarry bitumens, such as the seepages of pitch and bitumen in India and along the Euphrates, which have been used since the earliest times. In this country there are a few ancient seepages, where all the volatile oil has disappeared, leaving a residual deposit of spongy bitumens, the mineral name of which is Elaterite. Patches of elaterite are to be seen in the crest of small anticlines in the Carboniferous Limestone of Windy Knoll, near the head of the Winyates Pass in Derbyshire.

In the Trinidad Lake area an enormous seepage of bitumens has formed a large pitch lake, which for many years has been worked for asphalt, another bitumen mineral. Of far greater importance, of course, are the still-sealed-off deposits of oil, which can be reached by boring when discovered by the geologist or prospector. In nearly all these oil-pools there is a quantity of natural gas, the oil and gas being trapped in the crest of the fold under considerable hydrostatic pressure, sufficient, when the pool is tapped, to force the oil out at the surface as a ' gusher ' or artesian flow.

The problem of the oil geologist is to investigate areas

where Tertiary rocks are abundant—Central America, Persia, southern Russia, etc.—and to map them in greatest detail, particularly those beds which are known to be good oil-bearers or to be kindly for oil. When the presence of such beds has been confirmed, the next job is to investigate structures, to trace folding and locate the crests of anti-clines. This is very difficult, as many of the oil-bearing areas are now in desert country, where the solid rock is rarely exposed and most of the structures are concealed under a cover of recent sands and gravels. When a preliminary survey has indicated a likely area, more precise methods of prospecting are applied. One of these depends on the principles already described in connection with earthquake waves. Earthquake waves and all tremors are propagated through rocks at velocities which are related to the density of the material. In a small area, and in shallow depths, sufficiently strong waves can be generated by small explo-sions. In an area where it is suspected from preliminary survey that there is an oil-pool, a boring is made somewhere near the suspected pool and a charge of explosive placed in it. At distances from the borehole, and along widely divergent lines, several automatic recording seismographs (instruments that record the passage of an earth tremor) are placed, and their timing mechanism synchronised. The charge in the boring is then exploded, and the shock of the explosion is recorded on all the instruments. The general density of the country rock is known from the survey work, and the rate at which the shock will travel through such rock is calculated. The distance from the explosion to each instrument is used to calculate the exact time the shock will take to travel to it. If one line from the explosion to the instrument crosses an oil-pool, the low density and liquid nature of the oil will cause the shock to travel more slowly than through the country rock, and the record of shock passage at that instrument will be later than the time calculated. Such a delayed record indicates an oil-pool along that line. A second boring is made at another place so that the lines along which the instruments lie will cross the first set. After the second explosion a new line will be indicated along which the oil-pool lies, and the only place that will satisfy both records will be around the place where these two lines cross. The method, of course, has many great refinements, but the above is the general principle. This method has been used with some success in searching for masses of iron ore in the Carboniferous Limestones of Cumberland. An explosion made in one mine and recorded in another will arrive before the expected time if the wave has passed through a mass of high-density iron ore, or will arrive on time if only local rock has been passed through.

One of the most interesting geological discoveries in connection with oil in recent years has been the realisation that many great oil areas have a second type of structure, very different from the anticlinal pools. In parts of America and Persia the oil is associated with ' salt domes '. So far as these have been investigated, they most closely resemble a volcano, in which the place of the magma and lava is taken by crystallised rock-salt. There is a central ' vent '—a circular plug of salt, cutting vertically through all the surrounding strata, sometimes reaching the surface, and having ' flows ' of fine salt running from it. In most cases the plug does not reach the surface, but still has a cover of Tertiary strata over it. The top of the plug is covered by a cap of gypsum, and along all the sides of the plug and over the cap there is a great concentration of oil. A ' dome ' field, such as the famous ' Teapot Dome ' and others of Mexico, consists of a crowded mass of producing wells covering the top of the dome and reaching down the roughly circular sides. The full structure and origin of these domes are still a matter of investigation, but the ordinary types of oil-field link up with them in one way at least. In most oil-wells, as the oil begins to peter out its place is taken by a flow of brine, and this association of oil and salt seems almost universal, suggesting that the oil originates in a drying marine basin and is mixed in the strata with salts, both rock-salt and gypsum, such as were deposited from the Triassic seas in Britain.

During the last twenty-five years there has been a careful

search for oil in Britain, but with little practical result. The rocks of the Lower Carboniferous often contain a moderate proportion of bitumen, and in some places small seepages of oil have been noticed. The elaterites of Derbyshire also gave support to the idea that these strata might be oil-bearing. A few areas were selected where the geological structure was such that if oil were present it would have a satisfactory ' pool ' in which to collect, and borings were put down to tap these areas. In Derbyshire, at Hardstoft, a small supply of oil was obtained, and smaller supplies have been found in the Central Valley of Scotland in the Edinburgh district. It seems likely, from all the evidence now available, that any oil formerly present in Carboniferous rocks will long since have escaped by seepage or dissemination in other strata, and it seems unlikely that any continuous supply will be found.

In the lower strata of the Carboniferous Limestone series, in parts of West Lothian, Midlothian and Fife, there is an interesting series of ' oil-shales '. In these muddy shales there are many solid oil products that can be recovered by distillation at high temperature. In 1851 James Young built a plant at Bathgate to distil the local Boghead coal, which was a rich, oily cannel (impure) coal, and in 1858 the oil-shale deposits near Broxburn, West Lothian, were discovered and tried in the distillation plant, in place of the Boghead Coal, then nearly exhausted. It was soon shown that lubricating oils, paraffins and paraffin wax could be produced, and a large industry was founded. At its maximum, about 3¼ million tons of shale were being distilled annually (in 1913), but by 1933 the output had fallen to 1½ million tons. The shales are by no means exhausted, and are still producing useful quantities of motor spirit, solvent naphthas, wax and paraffin oils.

These oil-shales are fine-grained, muddy sediments, accumulated in lagoons and estuaries, in very shallow water. These waters received much broken-up carbonaceous matter from decaying plants and animals, which impregnated the muds, and which is the actual source of the oil. The oil-shales are very localised in their occurrence, and there seems to be have been no other area where the conditions were just right for their formation.

Geological Prospecting.

The miner and the geologist meet on the common ground of prospecting for minerals; the ' old-time ' prospector working by rule-of-thumb methods brought to the job a high skill gained by experience, the geologist working by methods that have been refined by theoretical as well as practical knowledge. The prospector who is searching for gold or other ores in a hilly country adopts a simple procedure which is actually the basis of much geological mapping. He utilises the eroding work of streams, which generally cut right through obscuring surface deposits of soil and gravels and expose solid rocks. Starting low down in the course of a stream that traverses suspected mineral-bearing ground, the prospector examines every boulder-bank in the stream and with his pan will wash and separate samples of sands, both coarse and fine, from the sand-banks and pools. Panning consists of taking a small amount of fine sand on to a hollowed shovel or in a small dish like a frying-pan and swirling it round in the water, at the same time tilting the pan slightly, in such a way that ordinary rock particles are washed over the edge by the current of water, but particles of heavier metallic ores or gold are left behind. It demands great skill and precision of touch to regulate the water currents just so that the ores are left, and nothing but long practice can give this skill. A sign of ore of any kind is generally called a streak, and a rich one would be a pay-streak. As soon as the miner has either a streak in his pan, or a fragment of vein rock, quartz, calcite or other rock gangue generally associated with ores, from the gravels, he knows that the stream is eroding, or has eroded, vein material higher in its course. He then proceeds upstream, watching his pannings and gravels, noting the increased frequency of streaks and the larger size of his gravels, until he either comes to an exposure of rock from which the stuff is derived, or finds that he has passed above it and got a part of the stream free from streak. His search is thus localised, and trial trenches and excavations will be made to locate an actual vein of mineral-bearing gravel. The geologist uses exactly the same methods, but may be attached to a large organisation to which he can send samples from time to time for accurate analysis and report, and he may have a useful knowledge of rocks and rock structures that can lead him quickly to likely country.

To this rough-and-ready prospecting, a precision method, of very wide application, has been added in recent years, which is more applicable to the discovery of large, buried masses of ore, or of dykes of igneous or ore-bearing rock that are not exposed at the surface. This is the method based on the observation of slight changes in the direction and amount of the force of gravity by means of an instrument devised by Eötvos, and brought into general use about 1923, called a " torsion balance ". The theory of this instrument and its measurements is highly mathematical, and cannot be attempted here, but its general use can be explained in simple terms.

The earth is held together and all things upon it are held to it by the force of gravity. If the earth were a perfectly uniform body with no differences in structure or level over its surface, the lines of gravitational force would be equally-spaced radial lines over all its surface, everywhere emerging exactly at right angles to the surface. In such an arrangement, which would be called a ' uniform gravitational field ', the introduction of any small mass of different density would upset the radial arrangement of the lines of force, and would both deflect them slightly from the perpendicular to the surface and also alter their value. In the complex structure of the earth's crust, the lines of gravitational force are almost everywhere deflected and variable, because of rapid changes in the density and shape of the rock crust. If we picture a dyke of heavy igneous rock, specific gravity about 3·0 or more, cutting up through an area of country, general specific gravity about 2·6, the edge of the dyke is clean cut and forms a sharp surface, across which the densities change; in such a condition there will be very marked disturbance of the lines of force from one direction to another—actually they will tend to crowd a little closer together over the higher density rock and incline towards it from the immediately adjoining areas of lighter rock. The Eötvos balance is an instrument that records not the actual force of gravity at any point, but the changes in direction and amount at two points very close together. By its use the changes mentioned as taking place across the edge of a dyke would be recorded, and when corrections had been made for the differences in surface levels and some other factors, the differences in density between the dyke rock and the country rock would be indicated, and something of the depth and position of the denser rock could be determined. The greatest application of the torsion balance has been to the investigation of structures in oil-country, and to the discovery of oil-pools. In this it has proved one of the most accurate instruments yet devised.

There are now other methods of prospecting also in use, but they are not essentially geological—the use of electric currents to measure changes in electric conductivity of the rocks, the conductivity rising rapidly where there are metallic deposits. Magnetic and resistivity measurements are also used, but all these belong more to the realms of physics than to geology.

CHAPTER XVI

Practical work : Simple equipment for field work; making notes and maps; recognising minerals; reference tables of mineral properties and rocks.

Field Notes and Maps.

THE evidence and material used as the basis of geological study are obtained from many sources—the disposition and structure of rock masses can be seen and recorded in sections that are exposed by the action of streams and rivers, in the sea-coast and inland cliffs, in quarries, mines, cuttings and in the material brought up from wells and deep bore-holes—wherever rock material can be seen *in situ* (*i.e.*, in undisturbed position), or can be collected and carried to the study and laboratory for further investigation. The geologist should therefore equip himself to make notes in the field and to collect material for home study. For this he will need a hammer, chisel, notebook, collecting-bags of linen or canvas or wrapping-paper, and a good strong satchel to carry his gear and specimens. A good type of hammer for all geological purposes has a head which is square in section, coming at one end to a square face, and at the other to a chisel edge, made at right angles to the shaft. It is useful to have a hammer of about 2 or 3 lb. weight, which is used for breaking off lumps from an exposure, the edge of the square face being used for this purpose and the chisel edge for splitting shales or fine bedded rocks, and a smaller ' trimming hammer ' about 6 or 8 ozs. weight with which to trim down the rough material got with the heavy hammer. For purposes of noting the position, directions of structures and dip, on a map, a compass is necessary, and a ' clinometer ' (slope measurer) for taking the *dip* or inclination of the strata.

A simple clinometer can be made from a wooden pro-tractor by adding a weighted pointer, free to swing about a suspension pin placed at the zero point of the protractor

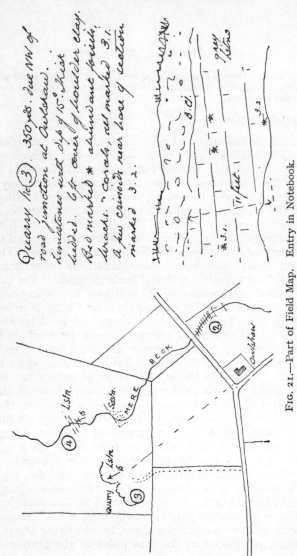

Quarry No. 3. 350 yds. due NW of road junction at Owlshaw. Limestones with dip of 15° West, tilted. 6 ft. cover of boulder clay. Beds marked * alluviant fossils "terrace." Corals, all marked 3.1. A few Crinoids near base of section marked 3.2.

Entry in Notebook.

Fig. 21.—Part of Field Map.

scale. When the edge of the protractor is placed along the bed of an inclined stratum, the pointer will swing into the vertical position like a plumb-bob; it can be fixed in position with the thumb as the instrument is lifted off to read the angle of dip from the scale. An ordinary protractor used in this way will give a reading which is the angle of the dip slope measured from the *vertical*, and this, subtracted from 90 degrees, will give the *true dip*, which is always measured *from the horizontal*.

In recording observations in the note-book or upon a map—and all students should try to make a geological map of a small accessible area as a basis for some of their field work—the first note should indicate accurately the position of the exposure. This can be done by giving the exposure a reference number on the map and using this for the notes in the book and for any specimens collected (see Fig. 21). The position on the map can be fixed either by a compass bearing from two prominent features seen from the position and marked on the map—*e.g.*, a near-at-hand cross-roads, house, barn, clump of trees or such mark —or sometimes a direction and the distance carefully paced along it from a fixed point will be sufficient. Quarries are usually marked on the map, and will need no such fixing. Next note the position and number of the exposure in the notebook (Fig. 21) and its nature—quarry, stream bank, temporary excavation, natural cliff, etc.; kind of rock exposed, nature of the bedding, direction and amount of dip. Then make notes of any other features—differences between one bed and another, position of specimens collected, giving them a further distinguishing number if necessary, as (1)3, with a sketch of the section showing the positions from which specimens were taken; if fossils are present, note whether confined to particular beds or not, whether abundant or rare, and again, positions found, with reference to the sketch section. Add remarks about the ' cover ' of the rocks—that is, the soil, gravel, clays or other superficial material seen at the top of the section. Wrap each specimen in paper to prevent them rubbing and scratching one another in the satchel, and mark the number of each carefully on one or two places on the wrapping-paper. Nothing is more disturbing than to spend time and trouble in securing important specimens for further examination, only to find on unpacking them that the place from which they were obtained has not been noted and is now forgotten. In the mapping it is best to use, whenever possible, the sheets of the Ordnance Survey, 6 inches to 1 mile, for making records of observations.

In recording geological facts in sketches and maps, certain symbols have been generally adopted for the principal types of rock, and a student is wise who learns these and sticks to their use in all his work. The diagrammatic shading of rocks is based upon certain simple characters. Shales are always thin bedded rock in thin layers with no well-marked vertical joints—it is therefore easy to see why shale is represented by close-set lines parallel to the bed. As the lines reflect the layers of the strata, they should follow the shape of the beds, slope with them, or follow their upper and lower surface round folds and bends, etc. Sandstones which are fragmentary rocks are shown by rows of dots, coarse or fine, to reflect the texture of the rock. Limestones with their well-marked horizontal bedding and prominent vertical joints are shown with a ' brick ' pattern. Igneous rocks with their lack of defined bedding and irregular jointing are generally shown by means of short dashes arranged in all directions. The symbol used to indicate the dip of a stratum is a short arrow, with the point placed on the position being recorded, and the dip in degrees is written against its stem. A fault is shown by a thick line with a short cross mark on the downthrow side. These symbols will be seen in the following diagram, and the structures to which they relate have been explained in earlier chapters (Fig. 22).

The earth's crust is formed of mineral matter which occurs in a variety of aggregated forms. It is composed for the greater part of about twenty different chemical elements, with minute traces of the other known elements present in proportions of less than one part in ten thousand of the bulk of the crust. Of the twenty commonest elements, oxygen and silicon are by far the most abundant, forming approximately 47 per cent. and 28 per cent. of the crust, respectively. Next to these in abundance are some of the metallic elements—aluminium, 8·16 per cent.; iron, 4·64 per cent.; calcium, 3·50 per cent.; magnesium, 2·62 per cent.; potassium, 2·35 per cent.; sodium, 2·63 per cent. No other element makes up more than a small fraction of 1 per cent. of the crustal material. These elements just listed are

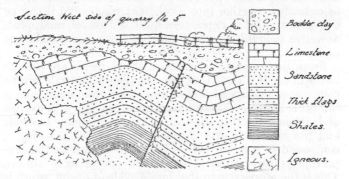

FIG. 22.—Notebook Section. Common symbols used.
Note reversed fault.

combined with silicon, oxygen or some other elements to form substances which have a constant chemical composition and with physical properties that can be measured or determined with accuracy and which are diagnostic of them. These simple compounds are called *minerals*. A *rock* is an aggregate of particles or fragments of one or more minerals, and the composition of a rock is frequently very variable, while its physical characteristics are by no means constant. A rock may be entirely crystalline with only a few different minerals present making up its bulk in definite and recognisable proportions—this is the case in most igneous rocks. The rock may be fragmentary, an aggregate of particles or grains of many different minerals, or even small fragments of rocks, which may or may not be bound together by a cement of some other mineral—most sedimentary rocks are fragmentary, as also are the volcanic ' ashes '. The constituents of a rock may vary in size over considerable limits, being either too fine for any recognition except under the microscope, or grading through all intermediate sizes up to those coarse conglomerates where the constituent boulders are some feet in diameter. In its geological meaning the term ' rock ' does not depend on the constituent materials being bound or cemented together into a coherent whole, and it can be correctly applied to deposits of sand and gravel, mud, peat, as well as to granites, sandstones and rocks that would come under the most popular definition.

From the proportions in which the elements are present in the crust, it is clear that the commonest minerals will be compounds of oxygen and silicon, with aluminium, and a few other metals. These compounds of metals with oxygen and silicon constitute the bulk of the *rock-forming minerals* and are mainly in the chemical form of *silicates*—i.e., a compound of a metal with silicon and oxygen in the proportion of two atoms of oxygen to one atom of silicon. This is the proportion in the simple oxide of silicon, which is the common mineral *quartz*.

To learn the properties by which minerals are recognised it will be advisable to work with a specimen of one or more rocks in hand. Secure a piece of *granite*, if possible; small fragments can often be got from the yard of a monumental mason for, at most, a few pence, and probably a piece having one side polished will be available. Remember, in getting your specimens from such a source, that ' granite ' as a trade name covers many igneous rocks that are not true granites, and so make it clear to the mason that you want an actual granite. Let us subject the specimen to careful examination. Granite is practically always light coloured, white to pink or red, or grey; black ' granites ' are usually other igneous rocks masquerading under a trade name. First notice that the rock is composed of crystalline particles, and that there are three obviously different kinds making up the rock. Each kind is distinguishable as being of approximately the same size, shape and colour, wherever it is found throughout the rock— such a texture of recognisable crystalline fragments is called holocrystalline (from the Greek word *holos*, meaning whole). The three minerals making up the granite are *quartz*, *felspar* and *mica*. We can distinguish these by the following several physical properties.

I. Colour.

Quartz: colourless and transparent. Felspar: white, grey, or pink. Mica: grey-brown to black.

2. Fracture and Lustre.

By fracture we mean the nature of the surface where a mineral is freshly broken; the following terms are used to describe fracture:

Conchoidal	. .	shell-like, curved concave or convex fractures.
Even	. . .	flat or nearly flat.
Uneven	. . .	rough with minute irregularities.
Hackly	. . .	set with spiky fragments.
Earthy	. . .	as in chalk.

Lustre is the quality of a surface as regards the kind and intensity of light it reflects, and is described as metallic, the lustre of metals; vitreous, the lustre of glass; resinous, pearly, silky or adamantine, the lustre of the diamond.

Quartz: uneven fracture and vitreous lustre. Felspar: uneven with a tendency to have many flat, platy surfaces which reflect light evenly as moved about. Lustre pearly. Mica: breaks in thin plates or leaves which reflect light with brilliance.

3. Cleavage.

This is the property that many minerals possess which enables them to split along certain directions more easily than in any other. An extreme form of cleavage is seen in the case of mica, where there is one very strong direction in which the mineral can be split into a number of thin plates or leaves, as thin as paper. In comparison with the ease of splitting along the cleavage, it is very difficult to break mica along any other direction. There may be more than one direction in which a mineral splits in this way; these are called cleavage directions, and will result, if three are present, in giving regular geometric-shaped fragments when the mineral is broken.

> Quartz: none. Felspar: two at right angles producing sharp rectangular edges. Mica: one very perfect forming thin sheets.

4. Hardness. Hardness is a very important property, and one which is easily tested. The student will find any time that is spent in familiarising himself with hardness and simple hardness tests is amply repaid when he comes to outdoor geology. Hardness can be tested with an old file. Rub a fragment of mineral or rock on the file. If it is soft, it will powder easily and quietly; if hard it will 'scratch' and screech noisily. To a sensitive ear the degree of noise and 'scratch' can give a close first approximation to hardness. The degrees of hardness have been related to a standard scale worked out by Mohr, and generally called by his name. In this scale ten minerals are ranged from the softest, No. 1, to the hardest, No. 10.

Mohr's scale.	Simple test.
1. Talc or graphite.	1. Marks paper, like a pencil.
2. Rock-salt or gypsum.	2·5. Finger-nail.
3. Calcite.	
4. Fluorspar.	4. Copper coin.
5. Apatite.	5·5–6. Window glass.
6. Felspar.	6·5. Good penknife blade, or
7. Quartz.	file.
8. Topaz.	
9. Sapphire.	9. Carborundum.
10. Diamond.	

The penknife forms the readiest test in most cases—it will be seen that the hardnesses 8, 9 and 10 are shown by gems, and these degrees will be wanted only on rare occasions, and by jewellers. In testing a mineral fragment place the knife *point* on the mineral with the blade nearly vertical. Press on firmly and make only a slight movement. Try out the tests on the granite. On the quartz the knife slips without making any impression; on the felspar a fine scratch is made with an effort, but on the mica it ' bites ' in and makes a deep cut.

Quartz, 7.   Felspar, 6.   Mica, 2·5–3.

The hardness of a mineral is tried against this standard set of minerals, all of which below 8 are fairly common. The thumbnail will scratch 1 and 2, glass will scratch up to 5, the knife can be used with discrimination to estimate many hardnesses below 6, by the degree of ' bite '. 5·5 would be estimated as a mineral that scratches 5 and is scratched by 6, and so on.

5. Streak. This is the colour of the powdered mineral. It is easily seen when the mineral fragment is rubbed over a white, unglazed porcelain tile or on a piece of ground plate-glass placed over a white paper. The colour of the powder is often very different from that of the solid mineral in the mass, and in some cases is the quickest way of differentiating two that are otherwise fairly similar.

Quartz: none.   Felspar: greyish-white.   Mica: colourless.

6. Crystalline Form. All minerals, if free to form without interference and under suitable conditions, will assume a crystalline shape, and each mineral has only one characteristic crystal form. A crystal of any mineral may, however, assume various shapes, due to more rapid growth in one direction than in another. Quartz will always crystallise in hexagonal prisms terminated by hexagonal pyramids; fluorspar or rocksalt will form cubes, felspar has a much more complicated form. The hexagonal prisms of quartz may be long and thin or very thick and stumpy, according as the crystal can grow more freely in one direction than in another, or they may be lop-sided, if one face has had greater freedom than the others.

As the crystal form depends ultimately on the arrangements of the atoms within the mineral molecule, some of its functions, such as the angles between the faces, the direction of cleavages and the optical properties of the mineral, are absolutely constant and capable of the utmost degree of precision in their measurement. The determination and description of crystal forms are a definite study, closely allied to mathematics and physics, and called crystallography, and only the elementary principles of the subject are needed in the earlier stages of geology to enable one to recognise simple crystal forms and to understand their description in general terms. For present purposes it is sufficient to give only a brief outline of the main classification of crystals.

All crystals can be classified under one or other of six groups or *systems*, according to the number and arrangement of the *crystallographic axes*—the lines around which the symmetry of the crystal is arranged. The systems are as follows:

Cubic : three axes, all equal, mutually at right angles.

Tetragonal : three axes, two equal lateral, and one vertical, all at right angles.

Hexagonal : four axes, three horizontal and equal at angles 120° to each other, and one vertical at right angles to the plane of the horizontal axes. The vertical may be the same length or longer or shorter than the horizontal axes.

Orthorhombic : three unequal axes all at right angles.

Monoclinic : three unequal axes, one vertical with one at right angles to it, the third making an oblique angle to the plane of the other two.

Triclinic : three unequal axes none at right angles.

This property of crystal form will be of little use in the study of rock specimens, but will have application in examining crystallised minerals such as are commonly found in mineral

veins. Occasionally in granite there are ' drusy cavities '—
i.e., cavities in which the constituent minerals have been
free to take crystal form, and then it will be seen that the
crystal forms are as follows :—

Quartz: hexagonal. Felspar: monoclinic. Mica:
monoclinic.

7. Specific Gravity. This property can be measured on
isolated fragments of the minerals, and though mainly a
laboratory test, a simplified determination can be carried
out in the field by means of a balance called after its maker,
Walker's balance. In this, a thin rigid rod is suspended
as a steelyard. A few lengths of cotton, and a glass or tin
of water, and a weight which can be a stone or lump of
metal will also be required.

The mineral to be measured is hung in a loop of thread,
and a counterpoise weight hung from the short arm of the
balance, so as to bring the mineral somewhere towards the
centre of the long arm. The position when the balance is
made is marked, and then, without moving the counterpoise, the mineral is immersed in water, and will need to be
moved farther along the balance arm from the fulcrum,
until a new position of balance is found. Measure the
length from the fulcrum to these two positions in any
units that are convenient, and call the first one, when the
mineral was weighed in air, a, and the second one, with the
mineral in water, b; then the specific gravity of the mineral
is given by the fraction $\dfrac{b}{b-a}$. Notice that by this method
no actual weights are needed, and the specific gravity is
determined only by the comparison of two lengths.

Returning to the rock sample we were examining, it will
be found that the specific gravities of the three constituents
are as follows:

Quartz, 2·65. Felspar, 2·75. Mica, 2·7.

For a long time the student will need to refer to tables
of mineral properties, when examining a specimen in the
field or in the study, and if the subject of mineralogy

is to be carried very far, a book on the subject will be needed. For all that is required for the purposes of this present book, however, and for most field work, the summarised tables that follow will be sufficient.

See Tables I, IIa and IIb.

The rock-forming minerals will prove to be more difficult of recognition than the ore minerals, as most of them are closely related complex silicates of several substances. The simple rule that acid minerals are generally light-coloured and of low specific gravity, and basic minerals are dark or black and heavy, will be very useful in dealing with rocks; it has of course no application to ore minerals.

The Principal Rock Types.

Rocks are much less definite in their composition than minerals, but they are still capable of arrangement into a few groups of closely related types. The first classification is by their mode of origin, separating three general types— igneous, sedimentary and metamorphic rocks. In each of these groups there are several varieties, of which only a few are of widespread occurrence and need be learned by the beginner in geology. The two main characteristics of a rock are the minerals composing it and the size or nature of the particles of those minerals, and the cement by which in some cases they are held together. For quick reference, rock types are tabulated for each group, and a description of the processes by which they are formed will be found in the earlier chapters of this book.

Igneous Rocks (fire-formed) are solidified from a molten mass, and are therefore made up of a few minerals of definite composition, occurring in crystals, and each of them recognisable. As silica enters into the composition of nearly all igneous rocks, the easiest division of them is made according to the percentage of silica present. The minerals with much silica, starting with quartz itself, which is pure silica, are light-coloured or transparent, with specific gravity about 2·6. As the amount of silica present in a mineral becomes less, the proportions of iron and magnesium increase, and as these are dark-coloured or black, and their minerals have a specific gravity about 3·3, we are able to

make a simple generalisation for a quick estimate of an igneous rock. Silica-rich rocks, called ' acid ', are usually light-coloured, and light-weight, silica-poor rocks, called ' basic ', are generally dark to black and very heavy. There is a group of ' intermediate ' rocks between these two extremes.

There is a second way of dividing igneous rocks, according to the way in which they solidified. When a molten mass cools slowly under great pressures, the minerals form large crystals; when the cooling is rapid and at atmospheric pressure, the crystals may be extremely small, even microscopic. We therefore make three divisions: *plutonic*—coarsely crystalline; *hypabyssal*—medium crystalline; and *volcanic*, finely crystalline, which correspond to deep seated intrusions, dykes and sills, and lavas, respectively.

See Tables I and III.

Metamorphic Rocks. Rocks which have been altered by heat and pressure. The heat usually causes the mineral composing a rock to recrystallise, and will sometimes change them into a simpler or more stable form. The pressure causes the new crystals to grow or to arrange themselves with their longest axis at right angles to the direction of pressure, so that the new rock has a very definite *grain* or cleavage in this direction. Igneous rocks are usually altered with much production of mica, so that the new types often glisten and shine from the presence of abundant small mica flakes.

See Table V.

Sedimentary Rocks. Accumulated on land or in water from the debris of pre-existing rocks. There are only four main varieties of sedimentary rocks, as follows:

Arenaceous	.	Sandy rocks, quartz the principal constituent.
Argillaceous	.	Clay rocks, clay the principal constituent.
Calcareous	.	Lime rocks, limestones and chalk.
Organic .	.	The accumulated remains or products of plant or animal life.

See Table IV.

REFERENCE TABLES OF COMMON MINERALS.

Table I.—Rock-forming Minerals.

Name.	Composition.	Colour.	Streak.	Hardness.	Specific gravity.	Habit.
QUARTZ	Oxide of silicon	None	None	7	2·65	Crystalline or massive
CALCITE	Carbonate of lime	White or creamy-yellow	White	3	2·7	Crystalline, cleaves into small rhombs
Felspars. ORTHO-CLASE	Silicate of aluminium and potassium	White to pink or red	White	6	2·6	Tabular crystals
PLAGIO-CLASE	Silicate of aluminium, sodium and calcium	White to grey	White	6	2·63	Tabular crystals
Micas. MUSCOVITE	Silicate of aluminium and potassium	White, brown or light green	None	2–2·5	2·7–3	Small platy crystals, sheets or thin plates
BIOTITE	Silicate of aluminium, potassium and magnesium and iron	Black or dark green	None	2·5–3	3	

REFERENCE TABLES OF COMMON MINERALS—*continued.*

Name.	Composition.	Colour.	Streak.	Hardness.	Specific gravity.	Habit.
HORN-BLENDE	Silicate of iron, aluminium, magnesium, potassium and sodium	Black or greenish-black	Pale greenish	5–6	3–3·4	Tabular crystals or fibrous
AUGITE	Silicate of aluminium, iron, calcium and magnesium	Black or greenish-black	White or greyish	5–6	3·3	Tabular crystals
OLIVINE	Silicate of iron and magnesium	Green or olive	None	6–7	3·5	Granular crystals

The above are the principal rock-forming minerals, and a quick distinction can be made between certain pairs of them, by very simple field tests. Calcite and quartz are the main constituents of limestones and sandstones, and an immediate test is that of hardness; all calcite rocks will scratch easily with a penknife, while quartz rocks will themselves scratch steel. Hornblende and augite are very similar in appearance, except for their cleavage, which in hornblende is approximately 120° and in augite 90°; the cleavage can generally be seen through a hand lens even in the small crystals of an igneous rock. The felspars are difficult to separate, but the colour may help; orthoclase tends to be pink or red, and plagioclase is generally white or greyish, even tending towards colourless in small fragments.

Table IIa.—Vein Minerals—Ores.

Name.	Composition.	Colour.	Streak.	Hardness.	Specific gravity.	Habit.
GALENA	Lead sulphide	Lead-grey and silvery	Lead-grey	2·5	7·5	Cubic crystals, cubic cleavage
COPPER PYRITES	Copper and iron sulphide	Brassy-yellow	Black	3·5–4	4·1	Small cubes, commonly massive
MALACHITE	Copper carbonate	Malachite green	Pale green	3·5–4	3·7	Massive, in rounded bosses
BLENDE	Zinc sulphide	Black or dark brown	White to brownish	3·5	4·0	Jet-black crystals, miner's 'black Jack'.
CALAMINE	Zinc carbonate	White to pale blue	White	5	4–4·5	Rounded, massive, incrusting or stalagmitic.
CASSITERITE	Tin oxide	Jet black	Whitish	6–7	6·6	Crystalline or in stream pebbles
WOLFRAM	Tungstate of iron and manganese	Greyish-black	Reddish-brown	5–5·5	7·5	Massive tabular crystals
PYRITES	Iron sulphide	Pale brassy-yellow	Greenish-grey	6–6·5	5·0	Commonly massive
HÆMATITE	Iron oxide	Black steel-grey	Red or reddish brown	5·5–6·5	5·0	Massive in rounded lumps—'kidney-ore'.
LIMONITE	Earthy iron oxide	Brownish-yellow	Light brown	5·5	3·8	Earthy ochre

Note.—The hardness figure is often given as, say, 5·5-6; this is usually an indication of rather variable composition in the mineral, which causes the hardness to vary somewhat.

Copper pyrites and iron pyrites will be difficult to distinguish by inspection alone, except that copper pyrites are usually more golden-yellow—the 'fool's gold' of the miner and prospector—and may also be spangled with other colours, often bright prismatic reds and greens, seen in a glancing light. These two minerals are, however, at once recognised by the streak and hardness, which are very different.

Table IIb.—Gangue Minerals.

Quartz and calcite already described are the commonest gangue minerals, only occasionally occurring together, but very commonly occurring with one or other of the following.

Name.	Composition.	Colour.	Streak.	Hardness.	Specific gravity.	Habit.
FLUORSPAR	Calcium fluoride	Translucent greens, purple, yellow, or colourless	White	4	3·25	Cubic crystals rarely massive.
BARYTES	Barium sulphate	Colourless, white, or may be stained yellowish	White	3	4·6	Tabular and platy crystals or massive.

Table III.—Igneous Rocks.

Minerals.	ACID.	INTERMEDIATE. (alkali)	INTERMEDIATE. (calcic)	BASIC.
Quartz	×	—	—	—
Orthoclase felspar	×	×	—	—
Plagioclase felspar	⊙	⊙	×	×
Mica	×	⊙	⊙	—
Hornblende	—	×	×	⊙
Augite	—	⊙	⊙	×
Olivine	—	—	—	×
Plutonic	GRANITE	SYENITE	DIORITE	GABBRO
Hypabyssal	QUARTZ-PORPHYRY	PORPHYRY	PORPHYRITE	DOLERITE
Volcanic	RHYOLITE	TRACHYTE	ANDESITE	BASALT

The upper column shows the minerals which compose the rock types directly below, in the lower columns; principal minerals in the rock ×; mineral which may be present ⊙; mineral not present —.

TABLE II. Sedimentary Rocks.

Rock type.	Name.	Constituents.	Remarks.
ARENACEOUS	Grit	Quartz grains	Very coarse, large grained, may have small pebbles present. Generally thick, massive strata. Coarsely bedded.
	Sandstone	Quartz grains	Finer grained, usually with grains cemented together with calcite or iron carbonate.
	Flagstone	—	A thin, bedded sandstone which splits off in even layers, or flags.
ARGILLACEOUS	Shale	Clay mud	Very thin-layered, splitting off in thin papery leaves. May have some mica flakes on the split faces.
	Mudstone	Clay mud	Like shale, except that the splitting property is entirely absent.
	Fire-clay	Clay and silica	The under-clay of coal seams, unbedded, full of fossil rootlets, free from lime and iron.
CALCAREOUS	Limestone	Calcite mud	Nearly pure calcium carbonate. Varies from coarsely crystalline to almost structureless, grey, cream or white, but may be darkened by organic impurities. Usually fossiliferous.
	Chalk	Calcite mud	Remains of innumerable microscopic creatures with a calcite skeleton, which formed a calcite mud or *ooze* in water free from other sediment. Almost entirely organic.
ORGANIC	Peat, Lignite, Coal	Plant remains	Plant remains which have undergone special chemical change, and with age and continued pressure pass through soft peat, to denser lignite (brown coal), and finally to coal. The change is accomplished by loss of oxygen and increase of the proportion of carbon.

Table V.—Metamorphic Rocks.

Normal rock type.	Metamorphic rock produced.	Remarks.
IGNEOUS ROCKS	GNEISS SCHIST	Coarsely crystalline, with the crystals streaked out in one direction. Finely crystalline, with abundant mica, and splitting in thin flakes and sheets.
SANDSTONES	QUARTZITES	The quartz grains fuse and recrystallise, and form a quartz rock of uniform texture.
SHALES	SLATES	The clay minerals are rearranged with flattened flakes all one way, so that the slate *cleaves* into thin sheets in a direction which may be entirely different from the original bedding.
LIMESTONE CHALK	MARBLE	The calcite is recrystallised to form a rock almost like an igneous one. Marble is easily distinguished from quartzite by its hardness of 3, quartzite hardness 6.

INDEX

(An asterisk indicates figure or table.)